James P. [illegible]

March 1934

THE

CHURCH ANTHEM BOOK

ONE HUNDRED ANTHEMS EDITED BY

SIR WALFORD DAVIES

AND

HENRY G. LEY

OXFORD UNIVERSITY PRESS
London: Amen House, Warwick Square, E.C.4
and 36 Soho Square, W.1

An edition of the words of The Church Anthem Book is published at One Shilling net, in cloth boards.

PRINTED IN ENGLAND BY
HENDERSON AND SPALDING LTD
AT THE SYLVAN PRESS
SYLVAN GROVE
LONDON
S E
15

CHURCH ANTHEM BOOK

MUSICAL EDITORS' PREFACE

THE aim of this book has been to choose and assemble one hundred approved anthems old and new within one volume of convenient size for choirs.

All the anthems have already been published, some of them in many different forms and editions. Choice has often been unhappily restricted by copyrights. In some cases, special words have been supplied. In the case of living composers, original editions have naturally been used. But in the case of 'classics' there is great diversity of choice. This diversity shows itself most in the keyboard accompaniment, and it has not been possible to bring the various editions into line in this respect. Some editors have the piano keyboard in mind, but most write for organ or other sustaining instruments. In the case of movements from works with orchestra, some editors have indicated instrumentation to help organists in registration; others have not. It has not been thought well to take these away in one case or add them in another. In short, re-editing has been generally avoided. Hints and notes as to keyboard accompaniments are offered at the end of this preface.

As Competitive Musical Festivals have conclusively proved of late years, there can be no village in the country, even of a few hundred inhabitants, that cannot render Wesley, Battishill, Handel, Bach or Brahms as well as Farrant and Tallis and Byrd, given the needed local enthusiast to lead. Choral zeal is fostered by hard work and a high standard. With such thoughts in mind, those responsible for this compilation have sought to give choirs a basic collection of anthems of many degrees of difficulty, chosen from among examples of all schools.

Both musical editors of this book had the good fortune to be trained in choice and usage by Sir Walter Parratt, whose tenet it was, at St George's Chapel, Windsor, to draw upon the finest examples, not only of our own country, but of every nation and type. It was therefore easy to rely for a first and basic selection upon anthems which had, through many years of testing, stamped themselves upon their minds as beautiful and fitting. For when hundreds of good anthems are repeated many times from youth upwards and become the subject of study in detail, the effect is two-fold and decisive. Compositions which pleased at first, but cannot stand searching tests, show their defects; whereas others endure not only because of their primal inspiration and attractiveness, but because of their proved workmanship. Even thus safeguarded by long practical testing, it is not possible to hope that this choice can be wholly satisfying; and, of course, defects of taste will always be reflected in defects of choice. Effort has been made to guard against personal shortcomings by much consultation, and by careful critical help from the committee and friends.

It may be helpful to add here a short list of other anthems suitable for different occasions and of varying degrees of difficulty, in the hope that many choirs will aspire to a far wider knowledge and use than could be encompassed within this book:

SUPPLEMENTARY LIST OF SUITABLE ANTHEMS

Composer	Voices	Anthem
W. G. Alcock	S.A.T.B.	Sanctus
Ivor Atkins	S.A.T.B.	*Almighty God, give us grace
Bairstow	S.A.T.B.	Save us, O Lord
Dutch Carol *arr.* A. E. Baker	S.S.	(3)This joyful Eastertide (Trebles only)
Battishill	S.S.A.A.T.B.B.	Call to remembrance
Battishill	S.S.A.A.T.T.B.	O Lord, look down from Heaven
Blow	S.S.A.T.B.	Salvator mundi
Bourgeois	S.A.T.B.	(6)O strength and stay
Boyce	S.S.A.T.B.	O where shall wisdom be found ?
Boyce	S.A.T.B.	(6)*Save me, O God
Boyce	S.A.T.B.	By the waters of Babylon
Bullock	S.A.T.B.	(2)Angels from the realms of glory
Byrd	S.A.T.B.	Have mercy upon me
Byrd	S.S.A.T.B	*Justorum animae
Child	S.A.T.B.	O Lord, grant the King a long life
Croft	S.A.T.B.	I am the Resurrection (Burial Sentences)
Gibbons	S.S.A.A.T.T.B.	*(4)Hosanna to the Son of David
Goss	S.A.T.B.	Lord, let me know mine end
Goss	S.A.T.B.	The Wilderness
Goss	S.A.T.B.	Almighty and merciful God
Alan Gray	S.A.T.B.	(2)What are these that glow from afar?
Greene	S.A.T.B.	Lord, let me know mine end
Greene	S.A.T.B.	O God of my righteousness
W. H. Harris	S.S.A.A.T.T.B.B.	(3)Fair is the Heaven
Harwood	S.A.T.B.	(7)O how glorious is the Kingdom
Harwood	S.A.T.B.	When the Son of Man shall come
C. Macpherson	S.S.	Awake my soul (Treble voices)
S. Marchant	S.A.T.B.	Ye holy Angels bright
Mendelssohn	S.S.A.A.T.T.B.B.	*My God, My God, why hast Thou forsaken me?
Mendelssohn	S.S.A.A.T.T.B.B.	*Why rage fiercely the heathen?
Mendelssohn	S.A.T.B.	There shall a star from Jacob come forth (Christus)
Nares	S.A.T.B.	The souls of the righteous
Nicholson	S.A.T.B.	(8)Who are these like stars appearing?
Ouseley	S.S.A.A.T.T.B.B.	*O Saviour of the world
Palestrina	S.A.T.B.	*Come, Holy Ghost
Parry	S.S.A.T.T.B.	I was glad
Parry	S.S.A.T.B.	*(3)Never weather-beaten sail
Parry	S.S.A.T.B.B.	*(3)There is an old belief
Purcell	S.S.A.T.B.	Jehovah quam multi sunt

Purcell	S.S.A.A.T.T.B.B.	(1)O Lord God of Hosts
Purcell	S.S.A.T.T.B.	O God, Thou hast cast us out
Purcell	S.S.A.T.B.	I will sing unto the Lord
Purcell	S.S.A.T.B.	Remember not Lord our offences
Stanford	S.A.T.B.	And I saw another angel
Stanford	S.A.T.B.	*(2)Glorious and powerful God
Stanford	S.A.T.B.	*(2)O living will
Stanford	S.A.T.B.	The Lord is my Shepherd
Steggall	S.A.T.B.	Remember now Thy Creator
Coleridge Taylor	S.A.T.B.	By the waters of Babylon
Travers	S.A.T.B.	Ascribe unto the Lord
Weelkes	S.S.A.T.B.B.	*(4)Hosanna to the Son of David
Weldon	S.A.T.B.	(4)Hear my crying
Weldon		In Thee, O Lord
S. Wesley	S.S.A.A.T.T.B.B.	*In exitu Israel
S. Wesley	S.S.A.T.B.	*Exultate Deo
S. S. Wesley	S.A.T.B.	All go to one place (edited Alcock)
S. S. Wesley	S.A.T.B.	The wilderness
S. S. Wesley	S.A.T.B.	Praise the Lord, my soul
S. S. Wesley	S.S.A.A.T.T.B.B.	He will swallow up death
	S.S.A.T.B.	For this mortal
Vaughan Williams	S.S.A.A.T.T.B.B.	(1)Lord, Thou has been our refuge
Wise	S.A.T.B.	Prepare ye the way of the Lord
Wise	S.A.T.B.	(5)The ways of Zion do mourn (edited Kitson)
Charles Wood	S.A.T.B.	(3)*Glory and Honour
Charles Wood	S.S.A.A.T.T.B.B.	*(3)'Tis the day of Resurrection
Charles Wood	4 soli and double chorus	*(3)Father all-holy
Charles Wood		(3)This sanctuary of my soul

(1) *Curwen.* (2) *Stainer and Bell.* (3) *Year Book Press.* (4) *Oxford University Press.* (5) *Bailey and Ferguson.* (6) *S.P.C.K.* (7) *Joseph Williams.* (8) *The Faith Press. All the rest Novello.*

*Unaccompanied

NOTE TO CHOIRS USING THIS BOOK

The place of an anthem is to bring beauty *heard* to the direct aid of the worshippers in the same way as church architecture and stained glass bring beauty *seen* to their aid. Just as the erection of a cathedral can be an act of devotion on the part of the architect, or stained glass windows on the part of the artist concerned, so the expert anthem should definitely, and by all concerned, be conceived, selected and prepared each week to dispose the mind of the hearers to worship. Such a conception sets its own standard of excellence. And precisely as a defect in a sacred building or in a window is a matter for immediate attention, whatever it cost in time, trouble and money, so should the perfecting of the anthem be a matter of careful preparation on the part of the Church authorities and their musicians. A higher choral standard is now being more hopefully and keenly felt in churches. The new opportunities to hear bad and good alike which the invention of broadcasting has brought about is speeding the change. It would not be so easy to offer counsels of perfection in this matter were it not for our knowledge of the increasing enthusiasm and contagion of delight in the finest choral work which is spreading daily. Choir-work can now become, through wireless, the pastime of music-lovers in every church of every denomination.

Doubts may linger in some minds as to the aim and appropriateness of this particular kind of work to the highest ends of worship, due possibly to unfortunate experience of the failure of particular teams. Human weakness often creeps in, so that the total impression of an anthem is merely: ' What a clever performance! ' This is, of course, as fatal as it would be in the case of merely clever pulpit oratory. But if display of skill is a danger, devotion is an infallible remedy and adds to the glory of it all. The team spirit itself is the cure. Where but four musical people (S.A.T.B.) are willing to perfect and to sing a few common chords, as an offering at a fitting moment in the act of worship, it can possess a thrill which nothing else can effect. To weave many chords together into a quiet anthem, illustrating and impressing some truth on the minds of the worshippers, involves a team-effort worth tireless practice in itself. A list of gramophone records is included in the alphabetical index. It is hoped they may be instructive both in interpretation and in learning individual parts.

DISCIPLINE

It cannot be too strongly urged that discipline is of primary importance in choir work Regular attendance at practice, is, of course, essential, and members of a choir must be prepared to sacrifice as much of their spare time as they can. The Competitive Musical Movement, which is so widespread to-day, has done much to produce the highest possible standard. It is hoped that this standard may be generally applied to the ordinary routine work of a choir, and that the prevailing custom of one full practice a week may be regarded as insufficient to meet the musical demands of to-day.

PRACTISING NEW ANTHEMS

In taking up a new anthem, let the whole choir read through all the words of the anthem aloud together two or three times, till the words fall into their natural rough unanimity of accents and quantities. This will not take long. It is well in the process slightly to exaggerate the natural features of the speech-rhythms till the choir has, as it were, stabilized on an agreed utterance that carries the spirit and sense of the words as simply as possible. A useful next stage is to speak the words *on a note* (unison). Then they can be chanted on one common-chord (S.A.T.B.)—the key-chord of the anthem for choice, and not pitched too high for any part. The natural accents, quantities and lights and shades of tone should still prevail. At this point a leader may give a down-beat upon any prominent syllable.

Such stages of preparatory practice can be intensely interesting; and indeed sometimes the finest words chanted euphoniously and expressively by a good choir can sound so lovely that when the composer's setting is taken up, it will sound for the moment actually disappointing, fettered by musical bars and shapes, and less natural than the preliminary practice. But this very fact will prove that the singers are sensitized to face the problem of carrying both words and music to their hearers. They have to interpret music, especially melody, together with the very words that brought the melody into mind.

When the problem of the words of any new anthem has been separately mastered, the actual music may be tackled, and in its turn sung *without the words*. Approach it as though the choir were an orchestra of individual instruments, whose whole concern is with the musical phrases and their perfecting. If the choir is so advanced and the anthem so straightforward and homophonic as to make it possible, the choir may well sing their own parts in *ensemble* from the first. But whenever need or opportunity offers for a difficult phrase of any particular voice to be taken by all the choir in unison, few methods of practice are better. Many anthems hold their musical treasure (as, for example, Wesley's 'Wash me throughly') in single phrases. For every voice, *sotto voce*, to join in practising the part in question in a beautifully phrased way, gives the whole choir increased interest and better hold of the work.

The third stage of choral study can then be wholly concerned with uniting the first beauty of the words with the first beauty of the music, without loss to either. When words and music have separately aroused keenness through study, it is possible to attain a higher standard all round. On the other hand, it is good from the first to seize every chance to think of and hear the chief melodic phrases of any inspired anthem as inseparably one in words and music. It is easy to break off, for example, in the first few minutes of verbal study as described above and to break out into music *plus* words. This is especially true of all declamatory phrases such as 'Fall down on us' in Mendelssohn's chorus 'Daughters of Zion'.

The rudimentary duties of a choir are expressed in the three words *timing*, *toning*, *tuning*. If it were desired to issue some very simple 'Army Order' for every member of every church choir in the fewest possible words, it might be well to condense it thus:

TIME EVERY CONSONANT
TONE EVERY VOWEL
TUNE EVERY NOTE } TO YOUR TEAM

There is a frequent order issued by choirmasters to choirs: '*sing out*'. A corresponding order should perhaps as often be issued and perhaps even more treasured: '*sing in*'. This is what a man does when in quiet talk with a friend he remarks on some fine melody: 'Isn't this lovely?' and sings a stave of it. *Singing-in* produces magical results when a whole choir sings as though they were all quietly showing a friend how beautiful this and that phrase can be.

KEYBOARD ACCOMPANIMENTS

The keyboard accompaniments in this book have not been arranged exclusively for anyone kind of instrument. With skill they will, it is hoped, prove helpful on this very account. Though the majority of churches now possess an organ with two or more manuals and pedals, some small choirs have nothing but a harmonium for accompaniment, and there is, happily, an increasing tendency to use the piano for accompaniment, since it is becoming clear that the larger and more resonant the church, the more beautiful it can sound when reverently handled.

A large number of the accompaniments supplied in this book are merely for use in early stages of practice, or 'trying over', and should not be used in service. In these cases organ, harmonium and piano should be reduced to their minimum level, whatever their possibilities. One stop should be used, and that a reticent one.

In the cases where accompaniment is essential, that is, where it is in some way made an integral part of the anthem, the arrangements here are of three kinds:

(1) those which set down the essential notes in due order without special regard for either kind of keyboard;

(2) those specially arranged for organ;

(3) those specially arranged for piano.

The editors would like to be allowed to offer a word or two to organists faced with an accompaniment more suited to the piano, and to pianists who have to adapt one specially suited to the organ.

MUSICAL EDITORS' PREFACE

The organist and pianist alike would do well to make careful comparative note of their own and each other's three chief means of giving *point* to accompanying phrases, *body* to accompanying colours (or chords), and *thrust* to accompanying rhythm. **1.** Point is given to phrases that matter: on the organ by duly prominent registration, on the piano by the calculated power and crispness of percussion. Here the piano scores. It is easier to strengthen one's touch at important points than to vary registration or work a swell box. **2.** Body is given to an accompaniment: on the organ by simply holding chords down in varying strengths as required, on the piano by the sustaining pedal. Here the organ scores when carefully managed, and at any point where a pianist would use the sustaining pedal to enrich a chord, the organist should study to furnish corresponding held chords with his left hand (probably on a swell or choir softer registration) while continuing to pick out and give point to the chief outlining phrases with his right hand and feet. **3.** Thrust is given to rhythms which matter for purposes of momentum (as in Brahms' ' We love the place '): on the organ by detached chording suited to the shorts and longs of the rhythm in question, on the piano by similar means. Here, perhaps, honours are easy as between the two; for, though the piano has more direct power by mere detached impacts to depict rhythmic figures, the organ is able to do it in an altogether more powerful and moving way, by strongly reiterated attacking of chords in the rhythm.

In addition to the above, it should be noted that whereas the organist supplies the harmonic basis of an anthem with the pedals, the pianist must use the octaves in the bass and below the compass of the voices if he is to supply important harmonic foundations. He should beware of overdoing this.

By such comparisons of the respective powers of piano and organ (and others can be deduced from or added to the above) the art of apt accompaniment on either instrument may best be learned. Above all, what the pianist does so delicately by touch in pointed phrasing and by use of sustaining pedal should be matched by the organist in his own organistic ways. Conversely the colour and mass at the disposal of the organist should be emulated by the pianist in pianistic ways. In all cases, the notes actually written in the present keyboard accompaniments should be freely changed, omitted or augmented for the sake of giving the voices nothing so redundant as to confuse eloquence, and nothing so sparse as to expose ' bare bones '. Accompaniment is sometimes essentially structural in an anthem—as in Wesley's ' Blessed be the God '. But it is more often an adornment.

An organ part for practice, etc., has been added to pages that are set out in vocal score, but not where the parts are in short score.

PHRASING MARKS. To assemble the work of so many writers—composers, editors and arrangers—in one book has brought together as many varieties in style and marking of phrasing. Bearing this in mind, and the fact that no two accompanists using the book will phrase alike, consistency of phrase-marking has seemed equally impossible and undesirable. But the plan adopted generally has been to refrain from adding phrase-marks (slurs, dots, lines) to the work of other minds, except in special phrases in some anthems, where a few marks seem to help to make clear the composer's melodic intentions. Even so, marks have been added sparsely rather than otherwise. In this matter, as in all the art of accompaniment, the golden rule seems to be to subject the use and all the relative lengths and strengths of every accompanying note to the needs of the voices and their rendering. And, as someone has playfully remarked, the best stop on the organ in the hands of the ideal organist is often ' stop altogether '.

Indulgence is asked from those who may be troubled at first glance by the crowded appearance of some of the pages in close score. One of the chief problems in the production of this book has been the presentation of a comprehensive list of anthems in a reasonable bulk, to sell at a price that makes it accessible to all. The inclusion of solfa notation has made the problem more difficult. It was agreed therefore to adopt close score for as many anthems as would lend themselves to this treatment, rather than to exclude many masterpieces from the book. As it is, the extent now exceeds by many pages that which was originally planned, and it is felt that the forgoing of the luxury of open score throughout the book is finally justified by the greater completeness of the contents as they now stand. Closer acquaintance with the pages by those hitherto accustomed to open score will, it is hoped, reveal the fact that once the eye is accustomed to following its own line on a stave, legibility is not impaired.

ACKNOWLEDGEMENTS

THE EDITORS desire to acknowledge most valuable help, in selecting these anthems and in preparing the volume for the press, given by the Committee on Public Worship and Aids to Devotion of the Church of Scotland, and especially that given so readily by the Conveners, the Rev G. Wauchope Stewart, D.D., and the Rev Millar Patrick, D.D., the Secretary, Mr W. M. Page and their musical advisers Dr W. Greenhouse Allt, and Mr Herbert Wiseman.

Thanks are also due to the following for permission to use copyright material: Dr Thomas Armstrong, Sir Edward Bairstow, Dr Percy Buck, Mrs Christina Cumming Cairns, the Committee of the Church Music Society, Professor E. J. Dent, Dr C. Armstrong Gibbs, Rev Dr E. H. Fellowes, Dr W. H. Harris, Professor C. Sanford Terry, Sir Richard Terry, Professor W. Gillies Whittaker, and Mrs Charles Wood. Also to the following Publishers: Messrs Bailey and Ferguson, Banks and Co., J. Curwen and Sons, the Faith Press, Messrs Novello and Co., the Society for Promoting Christian Knowledge, and the Year Book Press.

THE CHURCH ANTHEM BOOK

ALPHABETICAL INDEX

The music of anthems marked † has been published on gramophone records.
Anthems suitable for unaccompanied singing are marked thus *

No.	*Anthem*	*Composer*	
1	Abide with me	William Sterndale Bennett	1
2	All glory, laud, and honour	Johann Sebastian Bach	5
3	*All praise to Him who came to save	Philipp Nicolai and Georg Gottfried Wagner	11
4	*Almighty and everlasting God	Orlando Gibbons	13
5	*Almighty God, who hast me brought	Thomas Ford	17
[39b]	Banish fear and sadness	Johann Sebastian Bach	194
6	*Blessed are the pure in heart	Henry Walford Davies	19
7	Blessed are they that mourn	Johannes Brahms	21
8	†Blessed be the God and Father	Samuel Sebastian Wesley	36
9	*Bow down Thine ear, O Lord	Antony Stepanovich Arensky	48
10	*Call to remembrance	Richard Farrant	52
11	†Cast thy burden upon the Lord	Felix Mendelssohn-Bartholdy	58
12	Christ, Whose glory fills the skies	Thomas Armstrong	60
13	†Come, Holy Ghost, our souls inspire	Thomas Attwood	69
14	*Come, O Creator Spirit, come	Thomas Tertius Noble	73
15*	Come, Thou Holy Paraclete Come, Thou Holy Spirit, come	Henry George Ley	77
16	Comfort, O Lord, the soul of Thy servant	William Crotch	82
17	*Dark'ning night the land doth cover	Louis Bourgeois	85
18	Daughters of Zion	Felix Mendelssohn-Bartholdy	88
19	Declare His honour	Henry Purcell	94
20	Eternal Father, who didst all create	Gustav Holst	109
21	From all that dwell below the skies	Thomas Attwood Walmisley	117
22	*God be in my head	Henry Walford Davies	120
23	*†God is a spirit	William Sterndale Bennett	121
24	*God so loved the world	John Goss	125
25	Grant us Thy peace	Felix Mendelssohn-Bartholdy	127
26	Hark, the glad sound!	Henry Walford Davies	133
27	He is blessèd that cometh	Wolfgang Amadeus Mozart	138
28	†He that shall endure to the end	Felix Mendelssohn-Bartholdy	151
29	*Hear Lord. Lord make haste to help us	Peter Ilich Tschaikowsky	155
[39a]	Hence thou noisome serpent	Johann Sebastian Bach	200
30	*Hide not Thou Thy face from us	Richard Farrant	159
31	*Holy, holy, holy	Franz Schubert	161
32	*Holy, holy, holy, Lord God Almighty	Peter Ilich Tschaikowsky	162
33	*I heard a voice from heaven	John Goss	171
34	*I know that my Redeemer lives	Johann Michael Bach	174
35	If we believe that Jesus died	John Goss	179
36	*If ye love me	Thomas Tallis	187
37	*Into this world of sorrow	Percy Carter Buck	190
38	*Is it nothing to you?	Frederick Arthur Gore Ouseley	191
39	*†Jesu, Joy and Treasure	Johann Sebastian Bach	193
40	†Jesu, Joy of man's desiring	Johann Sebastian Bach	202
41	*†Jesu, Lamb of God, Redeemer	William Byrd	212
42	†Jesu, Lamb of God, Redeemer	Wolfgang Amadeus Mozart	219
43	*Jesu, lead my footsteps ever	Johann Sebastian Bach	223
44	Jesu! the very thought is sweet	Tommaso Ludovico da Vittoria	228
45	*Jesu! the very thought is sweet	Piae Cantiones, *arr.* Charles Wood	231
46	Jesu, the very thought of Thee	Edward Cuthbert Bairstow	234

No.	Anthem	Composer	
47	*†Judge me, O God	Felix Mendelssohn–Bartholdy	236
48	King of glory, King of peace	Johann Sebastian Bach	246
49	†Lead me, Lord	Samuel Sebastian Wesley	252
50	*Let Thy merciful ears	Thomas Weelkes	255
51	Let us now praise famous men	Ralph Vaughan Williams	257
52	Lo, round the throne	Henry George Ley	260
53	Lo! star-led chiefs	William Crotch	267
54	*†Lord, for Thy tender mercies' sake	*School of* Dr Tye	277
55	†Lord, it belongs not to my care	Henry Walford Davies	279
56	Lord, I flee to Thee for refuge	Felix Mendelssohn–Bartholdy	285
[56a]	Lord, my trust is in Thy mercy		293
[8a]	Love one another	Samuel Sebastian Wesley	39
57	Man that is born of a woman	Samuel Sebastian Wesley	307
58	*Most glorious Lord of Lyfe!	Cecil Armstrong Gibbs	311
59	*My soul, there is a country	Charles Hubert Hastings Parry	315
60	‡Now that the sun hath veil'd his light	Henry Purcell	326
61	*Now to the earth in mercy	Percy Carter Buck	333
62	*O Christ, who art the light and day	William Byrd	335
63	*O gladsome light, O grace	Louis Bourgeois	340
64	*O God of Bethel	Christopher Tye	342
65	O God, Thou faithful God	Johann Sebastian Bach	345
66	‡O Lord God	Percy Carter Buck	351
67	*O Lord, increase my faith	Orlando Gibbons	354
68	*O Lord, my God	Samuel Sebastian Wesley	358
69	*O Lord my God, to Thee do I lift up my soul	*Attributed to* Jacques Arcadelt	361
70	*O Lord, support us	Maurice Besly	363
71	*†O Lord, the maker of all thing	William Mundy	365
72	O Saviour of the world	John Goss	369
73	*O Saviour of the world	Giovanni Pierluigi Sante da Palestrina	372
74	*O that I knew where I might find Him!	William Sterndale Bennett	375
75	O what their joy and their glory must be	William Henry Harris	384
[19a]	O worship the Lord	Henry Purcell	100
76	‡Rejoice in the Lord alway	Henry George Ley	402
77	†Rejoice in the Lord alway	Henry Purcell	407
78	*Round me falls the night	Adam Drese	419
79	Subdue us by Thy goodness	Johann Sebastian Bach	421
80	The day draws on with golden light	Edward Cuthbert Bairstow	427
81	†The heavens declare the Creator's glory	Ludwig van Beethoven	432
82	The Lord is my shepherd	Samuel Sebastian Wesley	434
[93a]	‡The sorrows of my heart	William Boyce	500
83	The souls of the righteous	Henry Walford Davies	440
84	The strife is o'er	Henry George Ley	445
85	*Thee we adore	Giovanni Pierluigi Sante da Palestrina	450
86	Their bodies are buried in peace	George Frederick Handel	454
87	Thou Judge of quick and dead	Samuel Sebastian Wesley	463
88	*Thou knowest, Lord	Henry Purcell	472
89	*Thou Lord our refuge	Felix Mendelssohn–Bartholdy	474
90	Thou visitest the earth	Maurice Greene	477
91	Thou wilt keep him in perfect peace	Samuel Sebastian Wesley	481
92	*Turn Thee again, O Lord	Thomas Attwood	487
93	Turn Thee unto me, O Lord	William Boyce	491
94	Turn Thy face from my sins	Thomas Attwood	511
95	†Wash me throughly from my wickedness	Samuel Sebastian Wesley	515
96	We love the place	Johannes Brahms	522
97	†When Jesus our Lord was born	Felix Mendelssohn–Bartholdy	539
98	*When to the Temple Mary went	Johann Eccard	543
99	‡Whence is that goodly fragrance?	Albert Edward Baker	556
100	*Ye that do your Master's will	Orlando Gibbons	561

‡ Trebles and Altos only.

INDEX OF COMPOSERS, EDITORS AND ARRANGERS

* Denotes an arrangement or edition by the person named
(*The figures refer to the Anthem numbers*)

Arcadelt, Jacques, 1490–1575
69 O Lord my God, to Thee do I lift up my soul (*attributed to*)
Arensky, Antony Stepanovich, 1861–1906
9 Bow down Thine ear, O Lord
Armstrong, Thomas
12 Christ whose glory fills the skies
Attwood, Thomas, 1765–1838
13 Come, Holy Ghost, our souls inspire
92 Turn Thee again, O Lord
94 Turn Thy face from my sins

Bach, Johann Michael, 1648–1694
34 I know that my Redeemer lives
Bach, Johann Sebastian, 1685–1750
2 *All glory, laud, and honour
39 Jesu, Joy and Treasure
40 Jesu, Joy of man's desiring
43 Jesu, lead my footsteps ever
48 *King of glory, King of peace
65 *O God, Thou faithful God
78 *Round me falls the night
79 Subdue us by Thy goodness
Bairstow, Edward Cuthbert
46 Jesu, the very thought of Thee
80 *The day draws on with golden light
Baker, Albert Edward
99 *Whence is that goodly fragrance ?
Beethoven, Ludwig van, 1770–1827
81 The heavens declare the Creator's glory
Bennett, William Sterndale, 1816–75
1 Abide with me
23 God is a Spirit
74 O that I knew where I might find Him
Besly, Maurice
70 O Lord, support us
Bourgeois, Louis, 1510– ?
17 Dark'ning night the land doth cover
63 O gladsome light, O grace
Boyce, William, 1710–79
93 Turn Thee unto me, O God
Brahms, Johannes, 1833–97
7 Blessed are they that mourn
96 We love the place
Buck, Percy Carter
37 Into this world of sorrow
61 Now to the earth in mercy
66 O Lord God
Byrd, William, 1538–1623
17 Amen, by, 38
41 Jesu, Lamb of God, Redeemer
62 O Christ, who art the light and day

Crotch, William, 1775–1847
16 Comfort, O Lord, the soul of Thy servant
53 Lo, star-led chiefs

Davies, Henry Walford
6 Blessed are the pure in heart
22 God be in my head
26 Hark, the glad sound !
55 Lord, it belongs not to my care
83 The souls of the righteous
Dent, Edward J.
27 *He is blessed
Drese, Adam, 1620–1701
78 Round me falls the night

Eccard, Johann, 1553–1611
98 When to the Temple Mary went

Farrant, Richard, *c.* 1530–80
10 Call to remembrance
30 Hide not Thou Thy face from us
Fellowes, Edmund Horace
4 *Almighty and everlasting God
71 *O Lord, the maker of all thing
50 Let Thy merciful ears
Ford, Thomas, 1580–1648
5 Almighty God, who hast me brought
Fritzsch, Ahasuerus, 1629–1701
65 O God, Thou faithful God

Gibbons, Orlando, 1583–1625
4 Almighty and everlasting God
67 O Lord, increase my faith
100 Ye that do your Master's will
Gibbs, Cecil Armstrong
58 Most glorious Lord of Lyfe !
Goss, John, 1800–80
24 God so loved the world
33 I heard a voice from heaven
35 If we believe that Jesus died
72 O Saviour of the world
Goudimel, Claud, *fl.* 1549–72
17 *Dark'ning night the land doth cover
63 *O gladsome light, O grace
Greene, Maurice, *c.* 1695–1755
90 Thou visitest the earth

Handel, George Frederick, 1685–1759
86 Their bodies are buried in peace
Harris, William Henry
75 *O what their joy and their glory must be
Henderson, Archibald Martin
9 *Bow down Thine ear, O Lord

Herman, Nicolaus, *c.* 1485-1561
52 Lo, round the throne
Holst, Gustav
20 Eternal Father, who didst all create

Ley, Henry George
{15 *Come, Thou Holy Paraclete
{15 *Come, Thou Holy Spirit come
17 *Dark'ning night the land doth cover
52 *Lo, round the throne
63 *O gladsome light, O grace
76 Rejoice in the Lord alway
78 *Round me falls the night
84 *The strife is o'er
100 *Ye that do your Master's will

Mendelssohn-Bartholdy, Felix, 1809–47
11 Cast thy burden upon the Lord
18 Daughters of Zion
25 Grant us Thy peace
28 He that shall endure to the end
47 Judge me, O God
56 Lord, I flee to Thee for refuge
89 Thou Lord our refuge
97 When Jesus our Lord was born
Mozart, Wolfgang Amadeus, 1756–91
27 He is blessèd that cometh
42 Jesu, Lamb of God, Redeemer
Mundy, William, *c.* 1591
71 O Lord, the maker of all thing

Nicolai, Philipp, 1556–1608
3 All praise to Him who came to save
Noble, Thomas Tertius
14 Come, O Creator Spirit, come

Ouseley, Frederick Arthur Gore, 1825–89
38 Is it nothing to you?

Palestrina, Giovanni Pierluigi Sante da, 1525–94
73 O Saviour of the world
85 Thee we adore
Palmer, Charlton
7 *Blessed are they that mourn
96 *We love the place
Parry, Charles Hubert Hastings, 1848–1918
59 My soul, there is a country
Purcell, Henry, 1658–95
19 Declare His honour
60 Now that the sun hath veil'd his light
77 Rejoice in the Lord alway
88 Thou knowest, Lord

Ramsbotham, Alexander
10 *Call to remembrance, O Lord
30 *Hide not Thy face
36 *If ye love me

Schubert, Franz, 1797–1828
31 Holy, holy, holy

Tallis, Thomas, *c.* 1510–85
36 If ye love me
Teschner, Melchior, *c.* 1615
2 All glory, laud, and honour
Tschaikowsky, Peter Ilich, 1840–93
29 Hear Lord. Lord make haste to help us
32 Holy, holy, holy, Lord God Almighty
Tye, Christopher, *c.* 1508–72
64 O God of Bethel
Tye, (*school of*) *c.* 1521-2
54 Lord for Thy tender mercies' sake

Vaughan Williams, Ralph
51 Let us now praise famous men
Vittoria, Tommaso Ludivico da, *c.* 1540–*c.* 1605
44 Jesu, the very thought is sweet
Vulpius, Melchior, 1560–1616
84 The strife is o'er

Wagner, Georg Gottfried, 1698–1756
3 *All praise to Him who came to save
Walmisley, Thomas Attwood, 1814–56
21 From all that dwell below the skies
Weelkes, Thomas, *c.* 1576–1623
50 Let Thy merciful ears
Wesley, Samuel Sebastian, 1810–76
8 Blessèd be the God and Father
49 Lead me, Lord
57 Man that is born of a woman
68 O Lord my God
78 *Round me falls the night
82 The Lord is my shepherd
87 Thou Judge of quick and dead
91 Thou wilt keep him
95 Wash me throughly from my wickedness
Whittaker, William Gillies
39 *Jesu, joy and treasure
40 *Jesu, joy of man's desiring
43 *Jesu, lead my footsteps ever
60 *Now that the sun
79 *Subdue us by Thy goodness
Wood, Charles, 1866–1926
45 *Jesu, the very thought is sweet

INDEX OF ANTHEMS
SUITABLE FOR VARIOUS SEASONS AND OCCASIONS

MORNING

5	Almighty God, who hast me brought	Ford
12	Christ, whose glory fills the skies	Armstrong
32	Holy, holy, holy, Lord God Almighty!	Tschaikowsky
80	The day draws on	Bairstow

EVENING

1	Abide with me	Bennett
17	Dark'ning night the land doth cover	Bourgeois
60	Now that the sun hath veil'd his light	Purcell
62	O Christ, who art the light and day	Byrd
63	O gladsome light, O grace	Bourgeois
70	O Lord, support us	Besly
71	O Lord, the maker of all thing	Mundy
78	Round me falls the night	Drese

THE CHURCH

19	Declare His honour	Purcell
23	God is a spirit	Bennett
68	O Lord my God	Wesley
96	We love the place	Brahms

ADVENT

3	All praise to Him who came to save	Wagner
18	Daughters of Zion	Mendelssohn
26	Hark the glad sound!	Walford Davies
76	Rejoice in the Lord alway	Ley
77	Rejoice in the Lord alway	Purcell
87	Thou Judge of quick and dead	Wesley
92	Turn Thee again	Attwood
37	Into this world of sorrow	Buck

CHRISTMAS

24	God so loved the world	Goss
26	Hark the glad sound!	Walford Davies
37	Into this world of sorrow	Buck
53	Lo! star-led chiefs	Crotch
61	Now to the earth in mercy	Buck
97	When Jesus our Lord was born	Mendelssohn
99	Whence is that goodly fragrance?	Baker

EPIPHANY (see CHRISTMAS)

53	Lo! star-led chiefs	Crotch
98	When to the Temple Mary went	Eccard

LENT

9	Bow down Thine ear	Arensky
10	Call to remembrance	Farrant
11	Cast thy burden	Mendelssohn
18	Daughters of Zion	Mendelssohn
24	God so loved the world	Goss
29	Hear Lord. Lord make haste to help me	Tschaikowsky
30	Hide not Thy face	Farrant
41	Jesu, Lamb of God, Redeemer	Byrd
42	Jesu, Lamb of God, Redeemer	Mozart
47	Judge me, O God	Mendelssohn
49	Lead me, Lord	Wesley
50	Let Thy merciful ears	Weelkes
54	Lord, for Thy tender mercies' sake	Tye (*school of*)
56	Lord, I flee to Thee for refuge	Mendelssohn
67	O Lord, increase my faith	Gibbons
72	O Saviour of the world	Goss
73	O Saviour of the world	Palestrina
92	Turn Thee again	Attwood
93	Turn Thee unto me	Boyce
94	Turn Thy face from my sins	Attwood
95	Wash me throughly	Wesley

PALM SUNDAY

2	All glory, laud, and honour	Bach
26	Hark, the glad sound!	Walford Davies
27	He is blessèd that cometh	Mozart

PASSIONTIDE

38	Is it nothing to you?	Ouseley
41	Jesu, Lamb of God, Redeemer	Byrd
42	Jesu, Lamb of God, Redeemer	Mozart
72	O Saviour of the world	Goss
73	O Saviour of the world	Palestrina

EASTER

3	All praise to Him who came to save	Wagner
8	Blessèd be the God and Father	Wesley
34	I know that my Redeemer lives	J. M. Bach
35	If we believe that Jesus died	Goss
58	Most glorious Lord of Lyfe!	Gibbs
80	The day draws on	Bairstow
84	The strife is o'er	Ley

WHITSUNDAY

13	Come, Holy Ghost	Attwood
14	Come, O Creator Spirit	Noble
15	Come, Thou Holy Paraclete / Come, Thou Holy Spirit, come	Ley
23	God is a spirit	Bennett
36	If ye love Me	Tallis

TRINITY

4	Almighty and everlasting God	Gibbons
31	Holy, holy, holy	Schubert
32	Holy, holy, holy, Lord God Almighty	Tschaikowsky

HARVEST

90	Thou visitest the earth	Greene

MARRIAGE

6	Blessed are the pure in heart	Walford Davies
8	Love one another	Wesley
22	God be in my head	Walford Davies
40	Jesu, joy of man's desiring	Bach
76	Rejoice in the Lord	Ley
77	Rejoice in the Lord	Purcell
82	The Lord is my Shepherd	Wesley

BURIAL AND REMEMBRANCE OF THE DEAD

7	Blessèd are they that mourn	Brahms
8	Blessèd be the God and Father	Wesley
33	I heard a voice from Heaven	Goss
34	I know that my Redeemer lives	J. M. Bach
35	If we believe	Goss
51	Let us now praise famous men	Vaughan Williams
52	Lo! round the throne	Ley
57	Man that is born of a woman	Wesley
75	O what their joy	Harris
82	The Lord is my shepherd	Wesley
83	The souls of the righteous	Walford Davies
86	Their bodies are buried in peace	Handel
87	Thou Judge of quick and dead	Wesley

NEW YEAR

89	Thou, Lord, our refuge	Mendelssohn

MISSIONARY

19	Declare His honour	Purcell
21	From all that dwell	Walmisley
24	God so loved the world	Goss
26	Hark, the glad sound!	Walford Davies

HOLY COMMUNION

41	Jesu, Lamb of God, Redeemer	Byrd
42	Jesu, Lamb of God, Redeemer	Mozart

I ABIDE WITH ME

HENRY FRANCIS LYTE
(1793-1847)

W. STERNDALE BENNETT
(1816-75)

NOTE: The *staccato* marks may well be taken to indicate lightness and clearness rather than shortness. [*Ed.*]

SOP. p con espressione
ALTO
I need Thy pres - ence ev - 'ry pass - ing hour;
TEN. p con espressione
sostenuto espressione
p con espressione
What but Thy grace can foil the temp-ter's pow'r?
What but Thy grace can foil the temp-ter's pow'r?
Who like Thy - self my guide and stay can be?
Who like Thy - self my guide and stay can be?

cresc.
Thro' cloud and sun-shine, a-bide with me,
cresc.
Thro' cloud and sun-shine, Lord, a-bide with me,
sf
cresc.
sf
dim.
rall.
thro' cloud and sun - shine, Lord, a-bide with me.
dim.
rall.
thro' cloud and sun-shine, Lord, a-bide with me.
sempre dim.
dim.
rall.
Maestoso
SOP.
ff
ALTO
I fear no foe, with Thee at hand to bless;
TEN.
ff
BASS
Maestoso
ff

Ills have no weight, and tears no bit - ter - ness;
Where is death's sting?
Where is death's sting? Where, grave, thy vic - to - ry? I
Where is death's sting?
tri-umph still,
Adagio molto
ff
tri - umph still, if Thou a-bide with me.
Adagio molto
ff

2 ALL GLORY, LAUD, AND HONOUR

St. Theodulph of Orleans c.1615
Tr. by JOHN MASON NEALE
(1818-66)

MELCHIOR TESCHNER c.1615
Arr. by JOHAN SEBASTIAN BACH
(1685-1750)

Key D

SOPRANO

ALTO

TENOR

BASS

f All glo-ry, laud, and hon-our To Thee, Re-deem-er, King, To
Whom the lips of chil-dren made sweet Ho-san-nas ring! Thou
art the King of Is-ra-el, Thou Da-vid's Roy-al Son, Who
in the Lord's Name com-est, The King and Bless-ed One.

rall.

Soprano Chorus, Semi-chorus, or Solo
To Thee before Thy Pas - - - - sion, They sang their hymns of praise;
L.H. 16'. 8'. (4'.) quasi pedale
To

Thee now high ex - alt - -
-ed, Our mel - - o - dy we
raise.
Thou

didst ac - cept their prais - - - - es; Ac - cept the prayers we bring,
Who

in all good de - light - - -
-est, Thou good and gra - cious
King.
rall.

SOPRANO
ALTO
TENOR
BASS
ff
All glo-ry, laud, and hon - our To Thee, Re-deem-er, King,
To Whom the lips of chil - dren made sweet Ho-san-nas ring!
Thou art the King of Is - ra - el, Thou Da-vid's Roy - al
Son, Who in the Lord's Name com - est, The King and Bless-ed One.
rall.

3 ALL PRAISE TO HIM WHO CAME TO SAVE

CHORALE

from the Motet 'LOB UND EHRE UND WEISHEIT'

PHILIPP NICOLAI (1506-1608)
Harmonized by
GEORG GOTTFRIED WAGNER
1698-1756

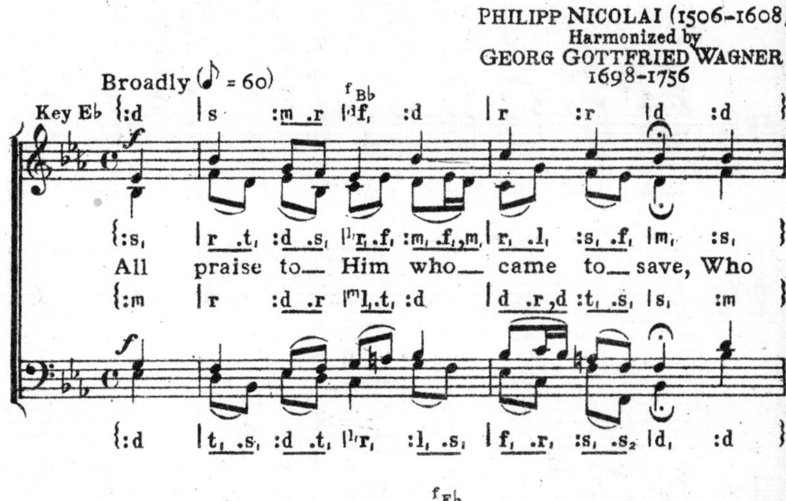
Broadly (♪ = 60)
Key E♭
All praise to — Him who — came to — save, Who

con - quer'd death and scorned the grave; Each day new praise re -

più f
-sound - eth To Him, the Life who — once was slain, The

This anthem may be sung unaccompanied.

Friend whom none shall trust in vain, Whose grace for aye a-
-bound - eth; Sing then, ring then,
F mi.
Eb t
p poco a poco cresc.
tell the sto-ry of His glo-ry, Till His prais-
-es Flood with light earth's dark-est pla - ce
ff allarg.
mf

ALMIGHTY AND EVERLASTING GOD

ANTHEM FOR FOUR VOICES

ORLANDO GIBBONS
(1583-1625)
Edited by E. H. FELLOWES
Very smoothly, but not slow. ♩= about 96
Key A♭
SOPRANO
ALTO
TEN.
BASS
Al-might - y and ev - er-last - ing
Al-might - y and
Al-might-y and ev - er - last - ing God, and ev - er -
Al-might - y and ev - er - last-ing God, mer - ci-ful-ly
God, and ev - er-last-ing God, mer - ci-ful-ly look
ev - er - last - ing, and ev - er - last-ing God, mer - ci-
-last - ing God, mer - ci-ful-ly look
look up-on our in - firm - i - ties, mer - ci-ful-ly look
up - on our in - firm - i-ties, mer - ci-
ful-ly look up-on our in-firm-i - ties, mer - ci-ful-ly look up -
up - on our in-firm - i - ties, mer - ci-ful-ly

From the Tudor Church Music Series (Oxford University Press) by permission.
Original: a minor third lower, but original pitch approximately as here.
To be sung unaccompanied.

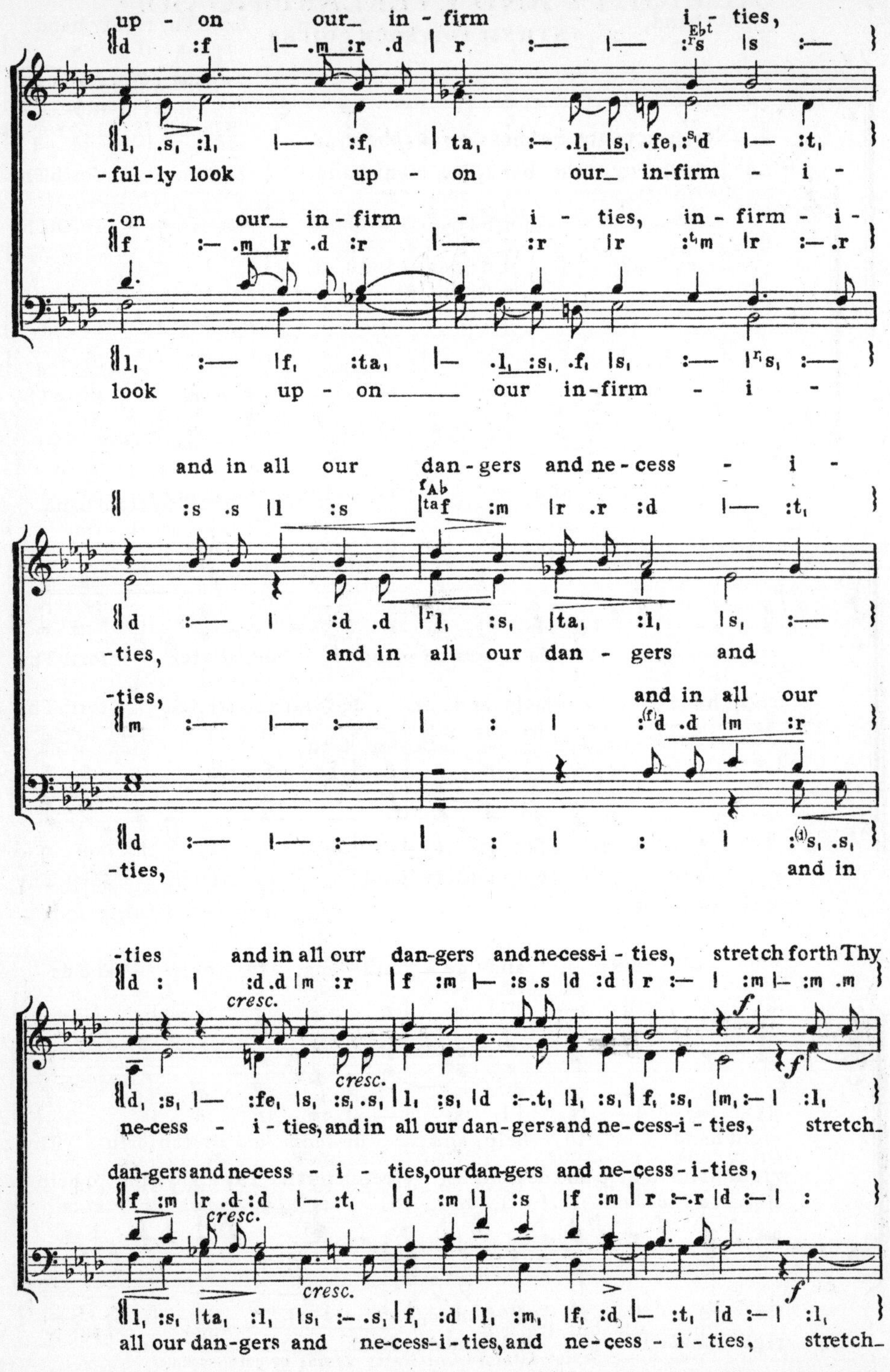

up - on our in - firm i - ties,
-ful - ly look up - on our in-firm - i -
-on our in - firm - i - ties, in - firm - i -
look up - on our in-firm - i -
and in all our dan - gers and ne - cess - i -
-ties, and in all our dan - gers and
-ties, and in all our
-ties, and in
-ties and in all our dan-gers and necess-i - ties, stretch forth Thy
cresc.
ne-cess - i - ties, and in all our dan-gers and ne-cess-i - ties, stretch
dan-gers and necess - i - ties, our dan-gers and ne-cess - i-ties,
all our dan-gers and ne-cess-i-ties, and ne-cess - i - ties, stretch
f

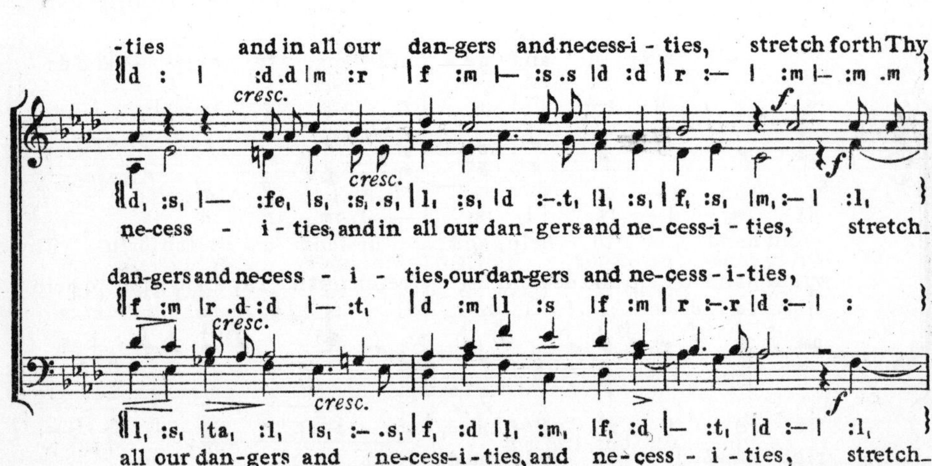

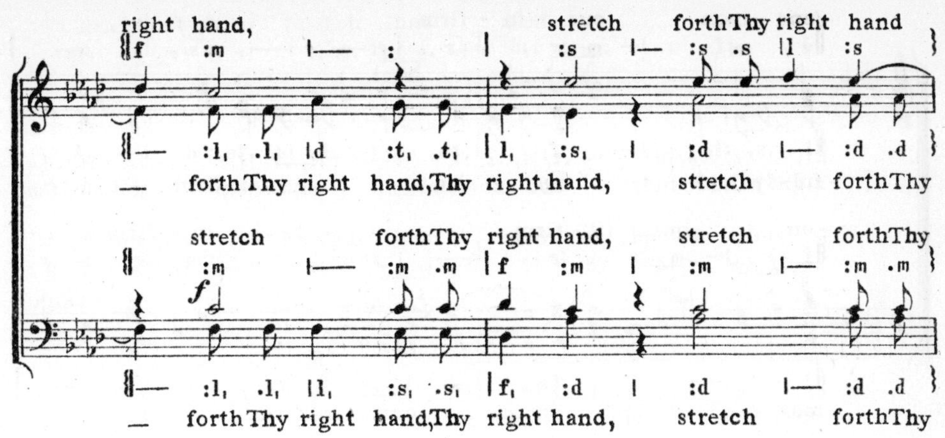
right hand, stretch forth Thy right hand
— forth Thy right hand, Thy right hand, stretch forth Thy
stretch forth Thy right hand, stretch forth Thy
— forth Thy right hand, Thy right hand, stretch forth Thy

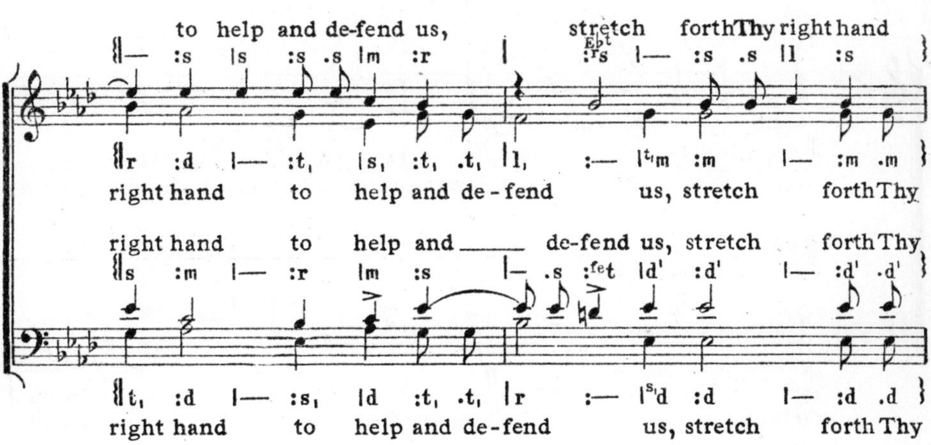
to help and de-fend us, stretch forth Thy right hand
right hand to help and de-fend us, stretch forth Thy
right hand to help and de-fend us, stretch forth Thy
right hand to help and de-fend us, stretch forth Thy

to help and de - fend us, to help and de -
right hand to help and de-fend us, stretch forth Thy
right hand to help and de-fend us, stretch forth Thy right hand to help
right hand to help and de - fend us,

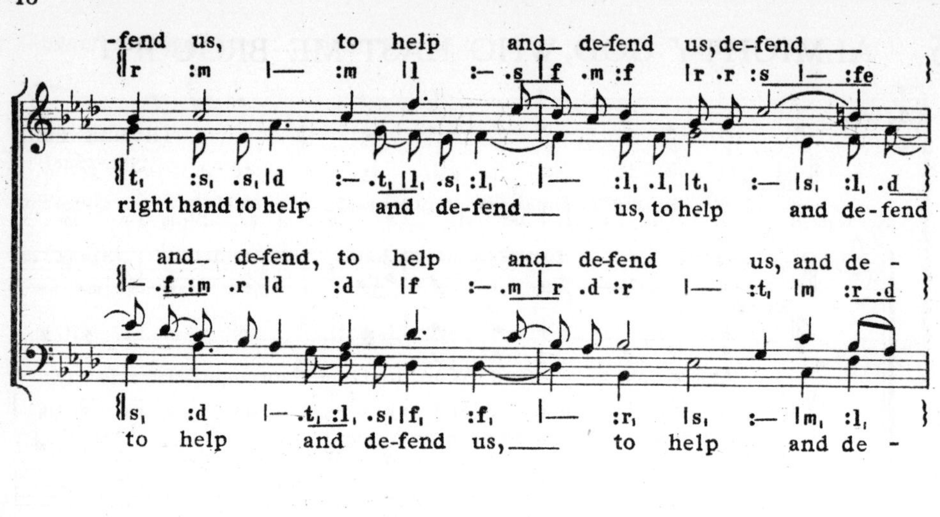
-fend us, to help and defend us, de-fend
right hand to help and de-fend us, to help and de-fend
and de-fend, to help and de-fend us, and de -
to help and de-fend us, to help and de -

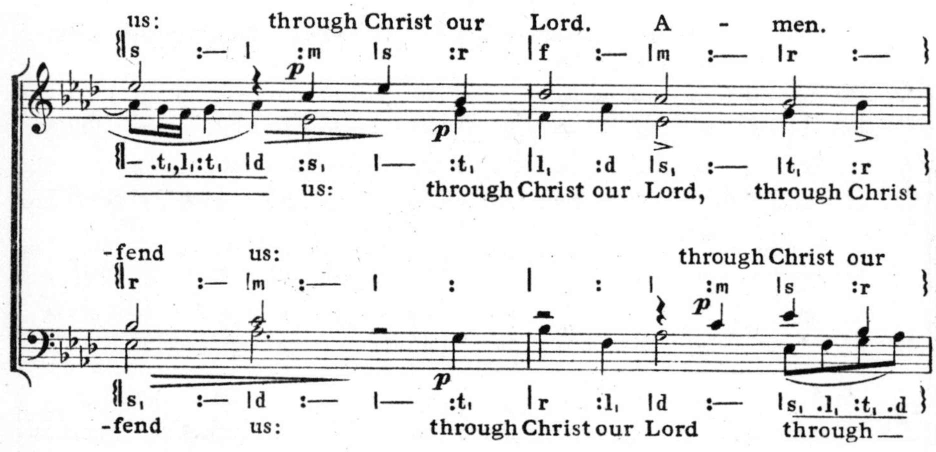
us: through Christ our Lord. A - men.
p
us: through Christ our Lord, through Christ
-fend us: through Christ our
p
-fend us: through Christ our Lord through

through Christ our Lord, A - men. A - men.
pp
our Lord, A - men. A - - men.
Lord, A - - men. A - men.
pp
Christ our Lord, A - men. A men.

5 ALMIGHTY GOD, WHO HAST ME BROUGHT

To be sung unaccompanied

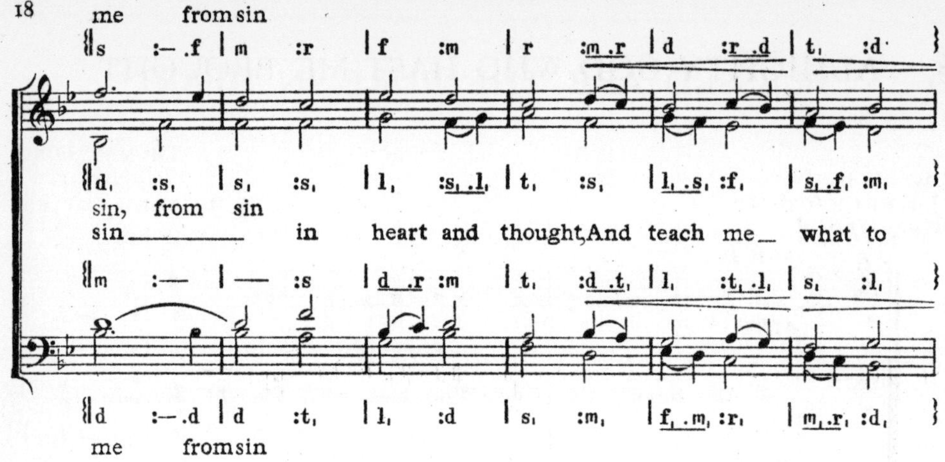

me from sin
sin, from sin
sin in heart and thought, And teach me what to
me from sin

Keep me from sin
mf
do and say, Keep me from sin, from sin
sin
in heart and
mf
Keep me from sin

dim.e rall.
pp
thought, And teach me what to do and say.
dim.e rall.
pp

6 BLESSED ARE THE PURE IN HEART

Words by
J. KEBLE
(1792-1866)

H. WALFORD DAVIES

Lord is theirs, Their soul is Christ's a - bode.
Still to the low - ly soul He doth Him-self im - part, And
for His cra - dle and His throne Choos-eth the pure in heart.
cresc.
pp
mf
mp

7 BLESSED ARE THEY THAT MOURN

Words adapted from St. Matthew v. 4 & Ps. cxxvi. 5-6,
by the Rt. Rev. the Bishop of Oxford
and STEUART WILSON

JOHANNES BRAHMS
(1833-97)
Arr. by C. Charlton Palmer

Andante moderato e con espressione (♩=80)

ORGAN

Cor. Str.

Celli & Bassi

Key F# d :s | – :f | f :r | – :t, | – :la, | – :s,

dim.

CHORUS

| d :– | – :– | m :– | – :– | f : | : | : | : | d :– | m :– | f :– | m :l | s :– | fe :– |

p SOP. *espress.*

Bless - ed, Bless - ed are they that

| m, :– | – :– | ta, :– | – :– | l, : | : | : | : | s, :– | – :– | d :r | s, :d | t, :m | – :r |

p ALTO *espress.*

Bless - ed, Bless - ed are they

| s :– | – :– | – :– | – :– | f : | : | : | : | m :– | ta :– | l :t | d' :m | m :s | t :– |

p TEN. *espress.*

Bless - ed, Bless - ed are they

| d :– | – :– | – :– | – :– | d : | : | : | : | d :– | – :– | – :– | – :l, | m :t, | – :t, |

p BASS *espress.*

Bless - ed, Bless - ed, blessed are

pp Str. Cor.

From Brahms' Requiem (O.U.P. edition)

mourn, for they shall_ be__ com - - - fort-ed. Bless - ed, Bless -
that mourn, for they shall_ be com-fort-ed, they shall be comfort-ed. Bless - ed, Bless -
— that mourn, for they shall be com-fort - ed__ they shall be comfort-ed. Bless - ed, Bless -
they that mourn, for_ they shall be com-fort - ed__ they shall be comfort-ed. Bless - ed, Bless -
Str.
Fl.
Cor.

Am i t
5 B♭mi
C5
f Dmi.
-ed they that mourn, they that mourn,
-ed they that mourn, they that mourn,
-ed they that mourn, they that mourn,
-ed they that mourn, they that mourn,
Str.
Tromboni
Ob.
Str.
for they shall be com - - fort-ed, they shall be
for they shall be com - - fort-ed, be com -
for they shall be com - - fort-ed, they shall be
for they shall be com - fort - ed, be com -
Fl.
Cor.

com - fort-ed.
- fort - ed.
In sor - row
com - fort - ed.
He that in sor - row, he that in
- fort - ed.
He that in sor - row, he that in
p
Str.
He that in sor - - row, sor - row
sow - eth, he that in sor - row, he that in sor - row
sor - row, that in sor - row, sor - row sow - eth shall
sor - row, that in sor - row sow - eth, in sor-row sow -
p cresc.
cresc.
f
Str. & Wind

sow-eth shall reap in joy shall reap in joy, shall
sow-eth shall reap in joy, shall reap
reap in joy in joy, shall reap in
-eth shall reap in joy in joy,
reap in joy, in joy, reap in
in joy, shall reap in joy, reap in
joy shall reap in joy in joy, shall reap shall
reap in joy, reap in joy, shall reap shall

joy.
joy.
reap in joy. Who go-eth forth in
reap in joy. Who goeth forth in
Str.
pp
Cor.
Str.
Who go-eth forth in weep-
Who go-eth forth in weep-ing, Who go-eth
weep-ing, in weep-ing, Who go-eth
weep-ing, in weep-ing, Who go-eth
espress.
Fl.
Ob.

ing, in weep - - ing,
forth in weep - ing, weep - ing,
forth in weep - ing, weep - ing, Who
forth in weep - ing, Who
Str. & Wind
Fl.
dim.
Str.
and
Who go-eth weep - ing
go - eth forth in weep - ing, forth in weep - ing
go - eth forth in weep - ing, forth in weep - ing
Fl.
ppp
p

cresc.
bear - eth, bear - eth forth good seed, bear - eth
and bear-eth, and bear-eth forth good seed, good
and bear-eth, and bear-eth forth good seed,
and bear-eth, and bear-eth forth good seed, good
Str. & Wind
seed, shall doubt - less come come a-gain with
seed, shall come a-gain with
shall doubt-less come a-gain with joy,
seed, shall doubt - less come a-gain with

joy, and bring his sheaves
joy, come with joy and
shall come a - gain with joy, come with
joy, shall come a - gain in joy,
with him, bring his sheaves with him.
bring his sheaves with him.
joy, and bring his sheaves, his sheaves with
come in joy, and bring his sheaves, his sheaves with
dim.

Bless - - ed,
Bless - - ed,
him.
Bless - - ed,
him.
Bless - - ed,
pp str.
Bless - - ed,
Bless - ed, Bless - ed are_ they that mourn
Bless - - ed, Bless - ed are
Wind

p espress.
cresc.
Bless - ed are they that mourn, for they
Bless - ed are they that mourn, for they
they that mourn Bless - ed are they that mourn, for they
Bless - ed blessed are they that mourn, for they
Wind
Cor.
Str.
dolce
shall be com - fort - ed. Bless -
shall be comforted, they shall be com-fort - ed. Bless -
shall be comfort - ed, they shall be com-fort - ed. Bless -
shall be comfort - ed, they shall be com-fort - ed. Bless -
Str.
Wind

-ed, Bless - ed are they that
-ed, Bless - ed are they that
-ed, Bless - ed are they that
-ed, Bless - ed are they that
Str. & Wind
mourn, For they shall be
mourn, For they shall be
mourn, For they shall be
mourn, For they shall be
Ob.
Str.
Fl.

com - - - fort-ed, they shall be com - fort-ed,
com - - - fort-ed, be com - - fort-ed,
com - fort - - - ed, they shall be com - fort - ed,
com - - fort - ed be - com - fort - ed,
Cor. p
Str.
Cor.
they shall be com - fort -
they shall be shall
they shall be
they shall
dim.
Wind p
Str.
Str.& Wind
cresc.
f
dim.
Without 16 ft.
add 16 ft.

C

-ed, shall be com - fort - ed,
— be shall be — com-fort - ed,
shall be, shall be — com-fort - ed, they shall be com-fort -
— be com - fort - ed,
Wind
Str.
cresc.
they shall be com-fort - ed, they — shall be com - -
mf
f
shall be com - -
cresc.
-ed they shall be com-fort-ed, for — they
mf
cresc.
they shall be com-fort-ed
p cresc.
Str. & Wind
f

- fort - ed, they shall be com - fort - ed, they shall be
- fort - ed, they shall be com - fort - ed, they shall be
shall be, they shall be com - fort - ed, they
com-fort - ed, they shall be com - fort - ed, they
Arpa
Cor.
Arpa
com - - fort - ed.
com - - fort - ed.
shall be com - - - fort - ed.
shall be com - - - fort - ed.
(8 and 16 ft.)
L.H.
R.H.

8 BLESSED BE THE GOD AND FATHER

I. Peter i. 3-5, 15-17, 22-25

SAMUEL SEBASTIAN WESLEY (1810-76)

L'istesso tempo
CHORAL UNISON
To an in - her - it - ance in - cor - rup - ti - ble and un - de -
- fil - ed, that fad - eth not a - way, re - serv - ed in
cresc.
heav'n for you who are kept by the pow - er of God, through
faith un - to sal - va - tion rea - dy to be re - veal - ed in the last

SOLO SOPRANO
time.
But as He which hath
Ped.
called you is holy, so be_ ye holy in all
manner of__ con - ver - sa - tion. Pass the time of your
pp
so - journ-ing here in fear, ___ in__ fear.__

E♭ t m Moderato (♩=104).

|| s: - | - : - | t : - | - : - | r' : - | - : - | s' : - | - : - | - : f' | r' : t | s : fe | f : r | d : — | m : f |

Love one an-

Clarabella

rall.

Sw. Reed

Ped.

|| s .s : — | s : d' | d' : t | l : t | d' : — .t,l | s : | s : — | s : l |

-o-ther with a pure— heart fer - vent-ly,

CHORUS. SOPRANOS

See that ye

|| l : s | f : — .m | m : — | r : | d : — | m : f | s .s : — | s : d' |

love— one a - no - ther,

SOLO

Love one an - o-ther with a

|| d' : t | l : t | d' : — .t,l | s : — | s : — | s : f | m : — | r : r |

pure heart fer - vent-ly,

CHORUS

See that ye love one an -

r :-.re|m :- |r :- |m :fe |s .s :- |l :t |d' :- |- :-
SOLO
-o - ther, Love one an-o-ther with a pure
Gmi.t
tm :- |- :- |m :-.r |d :d |l :- |s :f |m :- |r :-
heart fer-vent-ly; a pure heart
fEb
r :-.re|m :- |ds :- |s :f |m :- |r :r |r :-.re|m :-
CHORUS
fer-vent-ly. See that ye love one an-o - ther,
fAb
sr :- |m :f |f :m |m :m |m :r |r :r |r :d |d :d
SOLO
see that ye love, that ye love one an-o-ther with a

E♭t

pure heart fer - vent-ly.

CHORUS (S.I.)

with a

CHORUS

(S.II.)

See that ye love one an - o - ther with a

pure heart, a pure heart fer - vent-ly.

Recit. ad lib.

B♭t

CHORUS, TENOR & BASS

Be-ing born a-gain, not of cor-rup-ti-ble seed, but of in - cor-

Gt.

f Eb   3 Eb mi

‖r .,d :d |ᵈs :-.s |s :— |s :— |d' :— :s, .s, |ᵈl, :l, .t, |d .d :t, .l, }

f

-rup-ti-ble, by the word of God; for all flesh is as grass, and all the

Reed Sw.

Fmi. t m

‖m :f .s |l :l, .t, |d :t, .l, |m : .t, |ᵗl, :— |l, .l, .l, . : .l, .l, }

3

glo - ry of man as the flow - er of grass. The grass with-er-eth and the

Eb t

‖l, ,l, —:—.,l, |l, :— |m, :— |m, :m, |m, :— |ʳs' : ‖

flow-er there-of fall - - eth a - way.

f Full Org.

f

Ped

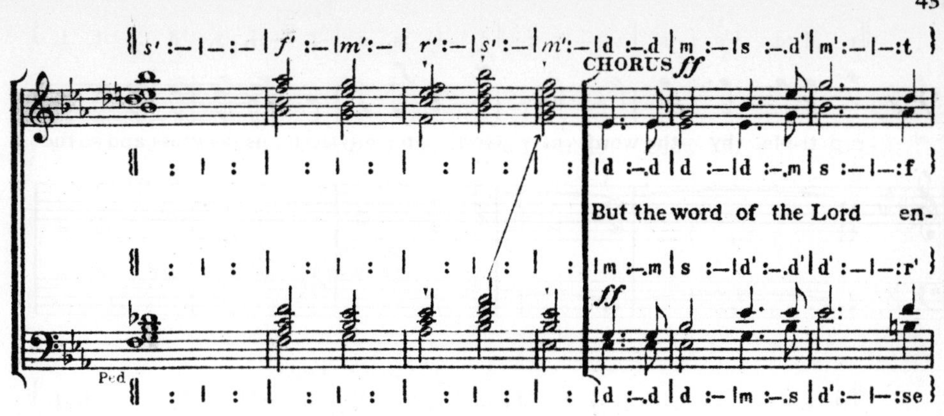

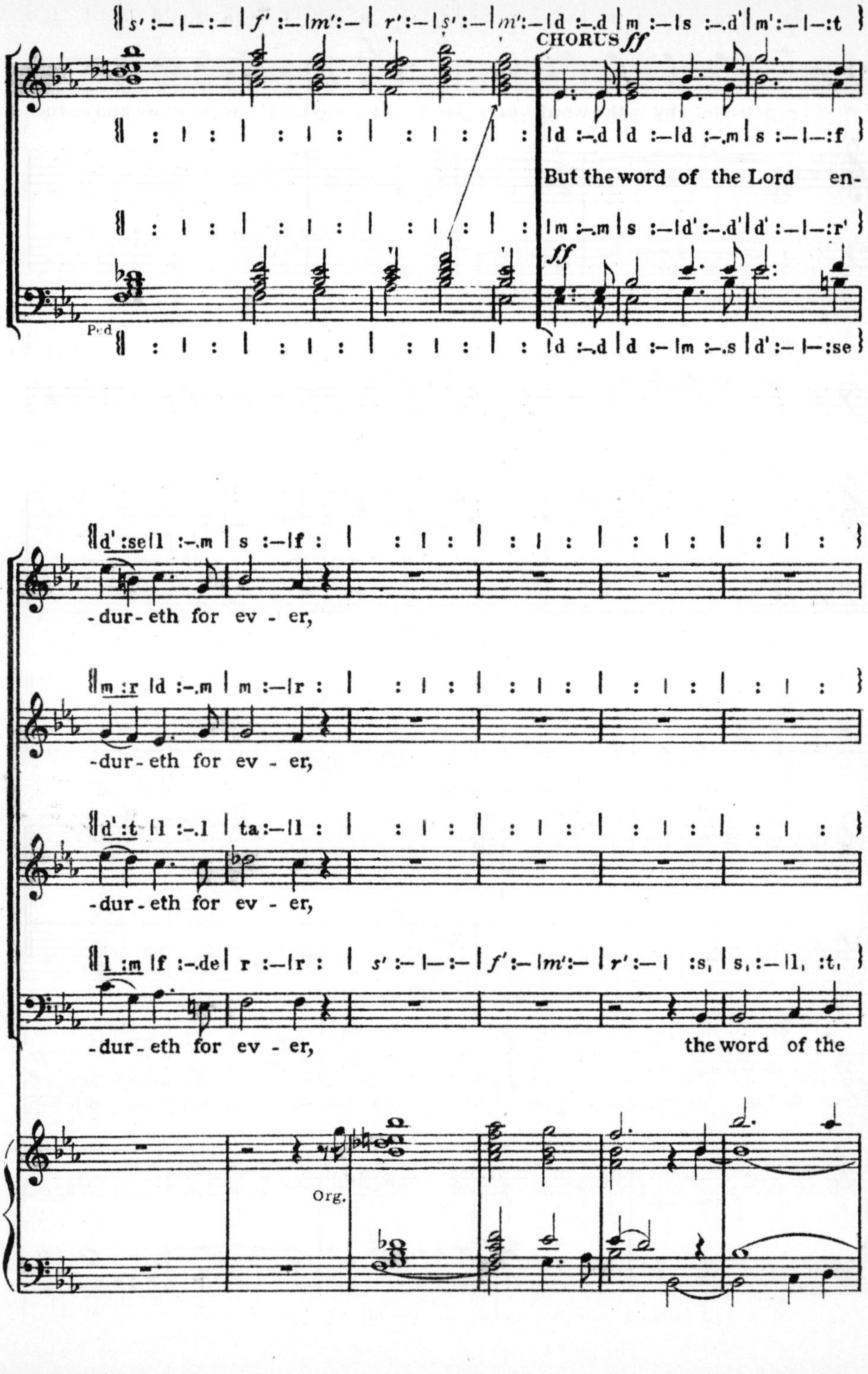

-dur-eth for ev-er,

-dur-eth for ev-er,

-dur-eth for ev-er,

-dur-eth for ev-er, the word of the

Org.

the word of the Lord en - dur - eth for ev - er, for
the word of the Lord en -
Lord en - dur - eth for ev - er, en - dur - eth for ev - er, the
ev - er, for ev - er, the word of the Lord en - dur - eth for
-dur - eth for ev - er, en - dur - eth for ev -
the word of the Lord the word of the
word of the Lord en - dur - eth for ev - er, en - dur - eth for

ev - er, en-dur - eth for ev - er, for ev - - er, en - dureth for
- - - - er, for ev - - - er, en - dureth for
Lord en - dur - eth for ev - er, the word of the Lord en - dureth for
ev - er, for ev - er, the word of the Lord en - dur - eth for
ev - er, the word of the Lord en - dur - eth for ev - er, en -
ev - er, of the Lord en - dur - eth for ev - -
ev - er, the word of the Lord en - dur - eth for ev - -
ev - er, the word of the Lord en -

-dur - eth for ev - - - - -
- - er, en - dur - eth for ev - er, for
- - - - er, en - dur - eth for ev - -
-dur - eth for ev - er, en - dur - eth for ev - -
- - - - er - more, en - dur - eth for ev -
ev - - - er - more, for ev -
- - - er - more, en - dur - eth for ev -
- - - er - more, en - dur - eth for ev -

-er - more, for ev - er, ev - - er -
- er - more, for ev - -
- er - more, for ev - er -
- er - more, for ev - er, ev - -
- more. A - - men, A - men!
- er - more. A - - men, A - men!
- more. A - - men, A - men!
-er - more. A - - men, A - men!

9

BOW DOWN THINE EAR, O LORD

Psalm lxxxvi. 1, 3, 5.

ANTONY STEPANOVICH ARENSKY
(1861–1906)

Edited and adapted to English words
by A. M. HENDERSON

-y. Be mer - ci - ful to me, O Lord,
-y. Be mer - ci - ful to me,
-y. Be mer - ci - ful to me,
-y. Be mer - ci - ful, O
for I do put my trust in Thee.
for I do put my trust in Thee.
for I do put my trust in Thee.
Lord, for I do put my trust in Thee.

For Thou, O Lord, art good and gracious, Of
For Thou, O Lord,_ art good_ and_ gracious, Of
For Thou,_ O Lord,_ art good_ and_ gra-cious, Of
For Thou, O Lord, art good_ and_ gra-cious, Of
great mer - cy un - to all,_ Of
great mer - cy un - to all,_
great mer - cy un - to all,_
great mer - cy un - to all,_

great and ten - der mer - cy to all, to
Of great mer - cy to all, to
Of great mer - cy to all, to
Of great mer - cy to all, to

all that call up - on Thee in truth.
all that call up - on Thee in truth.
all that call up - on Thee in truth.
all that call up - on Thee in truth.

17326

10 CALL TO REMEMBRANCE O LORD

Psalm xxv, 5. 6.

RICHARD FARRANT
(d. 1580)
Edited by A. RAMSBOTHAM

Original notation: a minor third lower.
From Barnard's 'First Book of Cathedral Music' (1641)
This anthem may be sung unaccompanied.

-mem-brance, O Lord, call to re - mem - brance,
mp
call to re-mem-brance, O Lord, call to re-membrance, O
mp
Lord, call to re- mem-brance, O Lord, O
mp
Lord, call to re-membrance, O
mp
O Lord, Thy ten - der mer - - cies and Thy lov - ing
mp
Lord, Thy ten - der mercies and Thy loving
mp
Lord, Thy tender mer - cies and Thy lov - - ing
mp
Lord, Thy ten - der mercies and Thy lov - ing kind -

kind - ness, which hath been ev - er of old, ev-er of
kind - ness, which hath been ev - er of old, which hath been
kind - - ness,
-ness, which hath been
B♭ mi.
old, which hath been ev - er of
ev - er of old, - which hath been ev - er of
which hath been ev - er of
ev - er of old, which hath been ev - er of

old. O re - mem - ber not the sins and of -
old. O re - mem - ber not the sins and of -
old. O re - mem - ber not the sins and of-
old. O re - mem - ber not the sins and of -
-fenc - es of my youth: but ac -
-fenc - es of my youth: but ac - cord - ing
-fenc - es of my youth: but ac - cord - ing
-fenc - es of my youth: but ac - cord - ing

-cord - ing to Thy mer - cy think
to Thy mer - cy think
to Thy mer - - cy think
to Thy mer - cy think
Thou on me, O Lord, but ac -
Thou on me, O Lord, but ac-cord - ing
Thou on me, O Lord, but ac-cord - ing
Thou on me, O Lord, but ac-cord - ing
mp

-cord - ing to Thy mer - cy think
to Thy mer - cy think
to Thy mer - - cy think
to Thy mer - cy think
Thou on me, O Lord, for Thy good - ness.
Thou on me, O Lord, for Thy good - ness.
Thou on me, O Lord, for Thy good - ness.
Thou on me, O Lord, for Thy good - ness.
rall.
p slower

II CAST THY BURDEN UPON THE LORD

QUARTET

He — is at thy right hand. Thy mer - cy, Lord, is

great; and far a - bove the heav'ns. Let none be made a -

- sha - med, that wait up - on — Thee!

12 CHRIST, WHOSE GLORY FILLS THE SKIES

CHARLES WESLEY (1707-88) THOMAS ARMSTRONG

No. A 56 of the Oxford Series of Modern Anthems. Reprinted by permission.

poco cresc.
Sun of right - eousness, a - rise,
Sun of right - eous - ness, a - rise,
Sun of righteous - ness, a - rise,
Sun of right - eous-ness, a - rise,
cresc.
mf
Tri - umph o'er the shades of night,
Tri - umph o'er the shades of night,
Tri - umph o'er the shades of night,
Tri - umph o'er the shades of night,
Gt.
16 ft.

dim.
Day - spring from on high, be
dim.
Day - spring from on high, be
dim.
Day - spring from on high, be
dim.
Day - spring from on high, be
near; Day - star, in my heart
near; Day - star, in my heart
near; Day - star, in my heart
near; Day - star, in my heart
Sw.
Gt.
Sw.

ap - pear.
ap - pear.
ap - pear.
ap - pear.
8ft only
BASS
Dark and cheer - less is the morn Un-ac-
Sw.
16ft.
TEN.
Joy - less is the day's re-turn, Till Thy
BASS
-companied by Thee;
Ch.

mercy's beams I see; Till they in - ward light im-
Till they in - ward light im-
L.H. Sw. with 16 ft.
Ch. R.H.
16 ft.
Glad my eyes, and warm my
- part, Glad my eyes, and warm my
- part, Glad my eyes, and warm my
Gt.
Gt.
Gt. to Ped.

f G mi. D4

marcato *f*

Vis -

heart.

heart.

heart.

sempre cresc.

- - it then this soul of mine,

mf Vis - it then this soul of mine, Pierce the gloom,

mf Vis - it then this soul of mine, Pierce the gloom of

mf Vis - it then this soul of mine, Pierce the gloom of sin and grief,

f *mf*

Fill me, Radiancy Divine, Scatter
Fill me, Radiancy Divine, Scatter
sin, Fill me, Radiancy Divine, Scatter
Fill me, Radiancy Divine, Scatter
all my unbelief; More and more Thy-
all my unbelief; More and more Thy-
all my unbelief; More and more Thy-
all my unbelief;
poco a poco cresc.
Sw.
Sw. with 16'
Ch.

mp
-self dis - play,
Shin - ing,
-self dis - play,
Shin - ing,
-self dis - play,
Shin - ing,
mp
More and more Thy - self dis - play,
Sw.
cresc. molto
ff
a tempo
Shin - ing to the per - fect day,
Shin - ing to the per - fect day,
Shin - ing to the per - fect day,
Shin - ing to the per - fect day,
Gt.
allarg.
dim.
Sw. mf a tempo
Gt. to Ped. in.

to the per - - - fect day.
to the per - - - fect day.
to the per - - - fect day.
to the per - - - fect day.
Ch.
Gt.R.H.
cresc. Gt.
rit.
cresc.
A - - men.
A - - men.
A - - men.
A - - men.

13
COME, HOLY GHOST
VENI CREATOR SPIRITUS
Tr. JOHN COSIN (1592-1672)
THOMAS ATTWOOD
(1765–1838)
Larghetto
1st VERSE
Key F
dolce
cresc.
Come, Ho-ly Ghost, our souls in - spire, and light-en with ce -
- les - tial fire. Thou the a - noint - ing Spi - rit art,
Who dost Thy sev-en-fold gifts im - part. Thy bles-sed unc - tion
from a - bove, Is com - fort, life, and fire of love, Is
com-fort, life, and fire of love.
p
f
Ped.
Diap.
Sw.

(Voices alone, Solo Quartet or Semichorus)
SOP.
ALTO
TEN.
BASS
dolce
cresc.
En - a - ble with per - pe - tual light, The dull - ness
of our blind - ed sight; A - noint and cheer our soil - ed
face, With the a - bun - dance of Thy grace. Keep far our
foes, give peace at home, Where Thou art guide, no
ill can come; Where Thou art guide, no ill can come.

ORGAN
CHORUS (with organ ad libitum)
dolce
Teach us to know the
Fa - ther, Son, And Thee of both to be but
cresc.
one, That through the a - ges all a - long, This
p
may be our end - less song; Praise to
cresc.
f

Thy — e - ter - nal me-rit, Fa - ther, Son, and Ho - ly
Spi - rit, Fa - ther, Son, — and Ho - ly Spi - rit.
ORGAN
Sw.

14 COME, O CREATOR SPIRIT, COME

VENI CREATOR SPIRITUS

9th century
TR. ROBERT BRIDGES
(1844–1930)

T. TERTIUS NOBLE

Molto sostenuto (♩ = 72)

Key A mi.
SOP.
ALTO
Come, O Cre-a - tor Spi - rit, come, And make with-in our
TEN.
BASS

hearts Thy home: To us Thy grace ce - les - tial give, Who
cresc.

of Thy breathing move and live. O Com-for-ter, that name is

Reprinted by permission of Messrs Banks & Son, Stonegate, York.
Words from the Yattenden Hymnal by permission.
To be sung unaccompanied.

ff
mf
Thine, Of God most high the gift di - vine: The well of life, the
tranquillo
p
fire of love, Our souls' a - noint - ing from a - bove.
mf
ff
Thou didst ap-pear in seven-fold dower, The gift of God's al -
f
migh - ty power: The Fa - ther's promise mak - ing rich with

sav - ing truth our mor - tal speech. Our sen - ses with Thy
light in - flame: Our hearts to heav'n-ly love re - claim: Our
dim.
bo - dies' poor in - fir - mi - ty, With strength per - pet - ual
pesante
for - ti-fy. Our earthly foes a - far re - pel, Give us hence-forth in

peace to dwell; And so, to us, with Thee for guide, No
ill shall come, no harm be-tide. May we by Thee, the Fa-ther learn, And
know the Son, and Thee dis-cern, Who art of both; And so a - dore In
per-fect faith for ev - er more. A - men. A - men.
rit.
a tempo
marcato

15 COME, THOU HOLY SPIRIT COME

Words 13th Century
Translations by
EDWARD CASWALL & MASON NEALE

Old German Melody. Arranged by
HENRY G. LEY

This Anthem is intended to be sung without accompaniment.

*These words may be sung if preferred

all our store, Come with-in our bo-soms shine, Hal-le- -

gifts be here: Come the soul's true rad-ian-cy, Hal-le -

- - lu-jah, Hal-le - lu-jah, Hal-le - lu-jah!

- - lu-jah, Hal-le - lu-jah, Hal-le - lu-jah!

CHORUS

Thou of Com-fort-ers the best, Thou the soul's most

Come, of Com-fort-ers the best Of the soul the

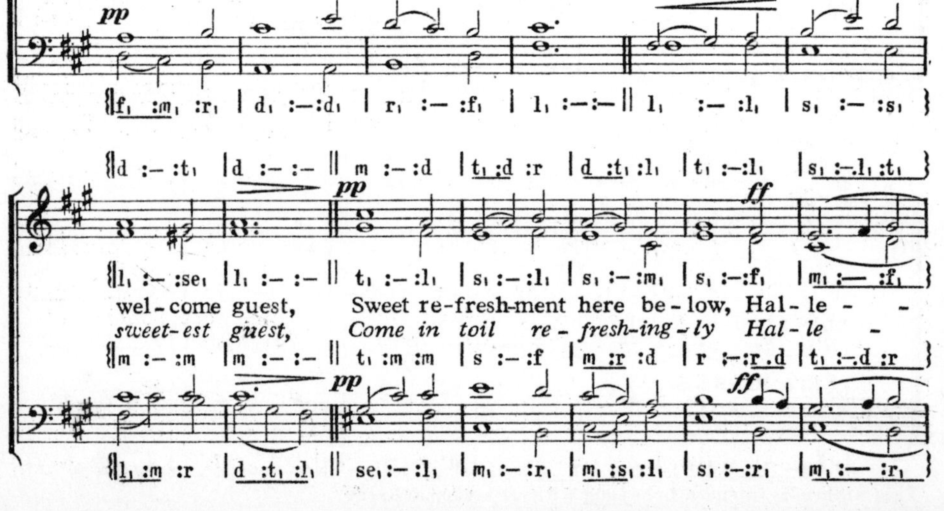

wel-come guest, Sweet re-fresh-ment here be-low, Hal-le -
sweet-est guest, Come in toil re-fresh-ing-ly Hal-le -

- - lu - jah, Hal - le - lu - jah, Hal - le - lu - jah!
- - lu - jah, Hal - le - lu - jah, Hal - le - lu - jah!
A little slower
Chorus or Solo Voices
In our la - bour rest most sweet, Grate - ful cool - ness
Thou in la - bour rest most sweet, Thou art sha - dow
Chorus or Solo Voices
poco rit.
a tempo
CHORUS
in the heat, Sol - ace in the midst of woe. Hal-
from the heat, Com - fort in ad - ver - si - ty. Hal-
- le - - - lu - jah, Hal - le - lu - jah, — Hal-
- le - - - lu - jah, Hal - le - lu - jah, — Hal-

f *a tempo*

- le - lu - jah! On the faith - ful who a - dore,
- le - lu - jah Fill the faith - ful who con - fide

and con - fess Thee ev - er - more, in Thy seven - fold
in Thy power to guard and guide, with Thy seven - fold

cresc. *ff*

gifts de - scend, Hal - le - - - lu - jah, Hal -
mys - ter - y, Hal - le - - - lu - jah, Hal -

ff

- le - lu - jah, Hal - le - lu - jah! Give them vir - tue's
- le - lu - jah, Hal - le - lu - jah! Here Thy grace and

sure — re - ward, Give them Thy — sal - va - tion, Lord,
vir - tue send; Grant sal - va - tion in — the end,
Give — them joys — that nev - er end, — Hal -
And — in Heaven fe - li - ci - ty, — Hal -
- le - - - lu - jah, Hal - le - lu - jah, Hal -
- le - - - lu - jah, Hal - le - lu - jah, Hal -
senza rit.
- le - lu - jah, — A - - - - - - men.
- le - lu - jah, — A - - - - - - men.
senza rit.

16

COMFORT, O LORD, THE SOUL OF THY SERVANT

from the Anthem 'BE MERCIFUL UNTO ME'

Psalm ixxxvi

WILLIAM CROTCH
(1775-1847)

Slow and soft

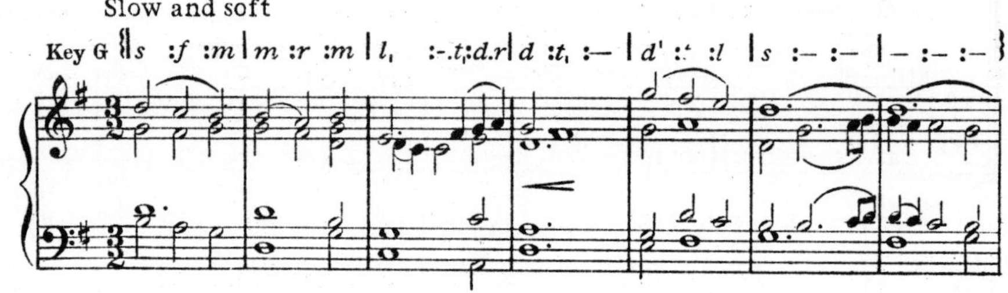

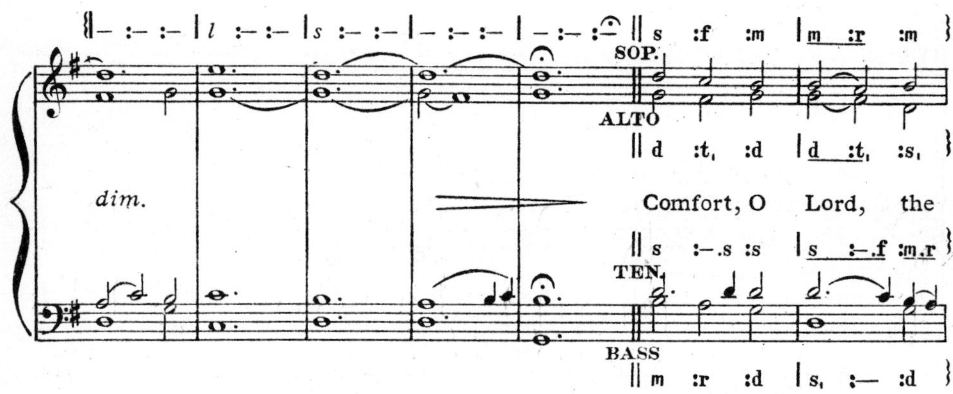

This Anthem may be sung unaccompanied.

Com - fort,
soul.— Com-fort, O Lord, the soul of Thy ser-vant,

B mi t
Com - fort,
for un - to Thee do I lift up my soul. Comfort, O

Lord, the soul of Thy ser - vant, for un - to Thee do I

lift up my soul, do I lift up my soul. — Com-fort, O

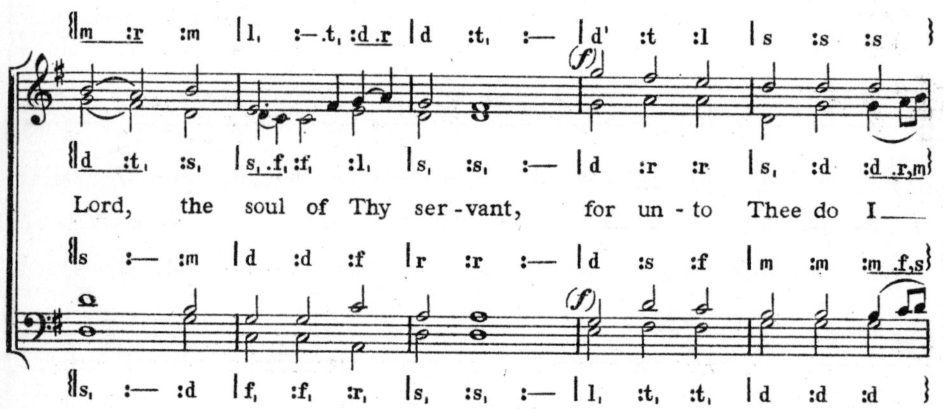
Lord, the soul of Thy ser-vant, for un-to Thee do I —

lift up my soul, do I lift up my — soul.

17 DARK'NING NIGHT THE LAND DOTH COVER

LOUIS BOURGEOIS (c.1510)
Set by CLAUD GOUDIMEL (c.1505–72)
Edited by HENRY G. LEY

Translated from the Greek
by ROBERT BRIDGES (1844-1930)

Moderato e sostenuto

Key A mi

Dark - 'ning night the land doth cov - er; Day is o - ver:
We give thanks, O Thou most High While with wonted hymn we a-dore Thee,
And im-plore Thee, For the light that doth not die.
Like a day our short life hast - eth: Soon it wast - eth:

Reprinted by permission of the Society for Promoting Christian Knowledge.
To be sung unaccompanied. Words reprinted from the Yattenden Hymnal by permission.

Com-eth sure - ly its sad eve: O do Thou that eve en-light - en,
Save and bright - en: Nor old age of joy be - - reave:
Come no pain nor pi - ty near it: Bless and cheer it,
That in peace we our peace win: As Thou wilt, do Thou us ga - ther,

Gracious Father, Only without shame and sin.
Now we pray for rest that sleeping in Thy keeping,
We may joy in the sun's ray. So thro' death's last darkness take us,
So awake us To heaven's ever-lasting day.
cresc.
rit.
Slowly
(From William Byrd's 'Ave verum')
A - - - - men.

88
18
DAUGHTERS OF ZION*
St. Luke xxiii. 28, 29, 30.
FELIX MENDELSSOHN-BARTHOLDY
(1809-47)
Andante con moto
Key G mi.
SOPRANO
ALTO
TENOR
BASS
Daughters of Zi-on, weep for your-selves,
weep for your-selves, and your chil - dren,
Daughters of Zi-on,
sempre stacc.
cresc.
weep for yourselves and your chil -
weep for yourselves and your chil -
weep for yourselves,
Daughters of Zi-on, weep for yourselves and your chil-dren,
* From the oratorio 'Christus'

-dren, weep for your-selves, and your chil - dren,
weep, for your-selves,
weep for your-selves, weep for your-selves. For sure-ly,
sure-ly the days are com - ing, when they shall ex-claim to the
dim.
cresc.

mountains: Falldown on us! Falldown on us!
and to the hills: Hide us! Hide us!
Daughters of Zi - on, weep for yourselves,
dim.
cresc.

dim.
rit.
a tempo
weep for your-selves,
Daughters of Zi - on,
Daughter of Zi - on, weep for your-
p
dim.
f
weep,
weep for your-selves, and your chil - dren,
-selves,
chil - dren, weep for your-
weep for your - selves,
Daughters of Zi - on, weep for your-selves, weep for your -
-selves, weep for your - selves, weep for your - selves,

and your chil - dren,
cresc.
-selves, and your chil - dren,
-selves, and chil - dren, Daughters of Zi-on,
cresc.
cresc.
— and chil - dren, weep for your - selves, weep for your-
cresc.
weep for your - selves, and your chil -
weep for your-selves, weep for your - selves, and your chil -
-selves, weep for your - selves, your-selves and chil -
-dren, weep for your - selves, weep for your-selves, O weep for your-
pp
pp

-selves, and your chil - dren!
weep, weep!
weep for your-
weep, weep!
weep for your - selves, your-
weep, weep, for your - selves, weep for your-
weep for your - selves, your - selves, and your chil - dren,
-selves, your - selves, your - selves, and your chil - dren,
-selves, your - selves, and your chil - dren, weep for your-
-selves, your - selves, and your chil - dren,
-selves, weep for your - selves!
cresc.
dim.
dim. e rall.

19 DECLARE HIS HONOUR

from 'O SING UNTO THE LORD'

Psalm xcvi. 3.6.4.5.9.10

HENRY PURCELL
(1658-95)

Maestoso

SOLO BASS — Quasi Recit.

Key F

BASS

ORGAN

mf

Declare His hon - our, declare His

hon - our, His hon-our un-to the hea-then, declare His

a tempo

hon - our declare His hon-our un-to the hea-then: and His

won - - - ders, His won - -

- - - ders un - to all ______ peo - ple.

Largamente

CHORUS

SOP.

ALTO

Glo - ry and wor - ship are be-fore Him.

TEN.

BASS

Largamente

Ped.

Glo - ry and wor - ship are be - fore Him;

Ami.
Dmi.
pow'r and hon-our, pow'r and hon-our
pow'r and hon-our, pow'r and hon-our
pow'r and hon-our, pow'r and hon-our
pow'r and hon-our, pow'r and hon-our
ff
are in His sanc - tu - a - ry.
are in His sanc - tu - a - ry.
are in His sanc - tu - a - ry.
are in His sanc - tu - a - ry.

Moderato
SOLI
SOP.
:d :m | f :s :s, | d .s, :m, :s, | d :— :— | — .,r :m :r .,d
ALTO
mf
The Lord is great, great, is
Moderato
mf Ground Bass

.m :d :m | s :— :— | .l :s :t | d' :—.t :d' .t
mf
The Lord is great, the Lord is great, and can-not
d :— :— | — .d :s, :d | t, .,d .r :— : | m :—.r :m .r
great, the Lord is great, great, and can-not

l .s :l .s :f .m | r :—.m :r | .m :d :m | s :— :—
worth-i - ly be prais - ed, the Lord is great:
d .t, :d .m :r .d | t, :—.d :t, | : : | :d :d
worth-i - ly be prais - ed. He is

He is more to be fear-ed, is more to be fear-ed, be
more to be fear-ed, be fear-ed, is more to be fear-ed, be

fear-ed than all, than all gods.

As for all the gods of the hea-then, they are, they
As for all the gods, the gods of the hea-then, they are, they

are but i - dols: but it is the Lord that
made the heav'ns, it is the
Lord that made the heav'ns, that made the heav'ns.
Lord that made the heav'ns, the heav'ns.
rall.
p
tr

Lento ma non troppo
SOLI
SOP.
mp
ALTO
SOLI
O wor - ship the Lord, wor - ship the
O wor - ship the Lord, O, O wor - ship the
TEN. mp
BASS
Lento ma non troppo
Broadly
CHORUS
mf
Lord in the beau - ty of ho - li-ness, O wor - ship Lord,
Broadly
O, O wor-ship the Lord in the beau - ty of ho - li-ness:

C mi.
G mi.
let the whole earth stand in awe of Him,
let the whole earth stand in awe, let the
let the whole earth stand in awe, let the
let the whole earth stand in awe, let the whole earth
Ped.
poco a poco dim.
let the whole earth stand in awe of Him,
whole earth stand in awe of Him,
whole earth stand in awe of Him, let the whole earth
stand in awe of Him, let the whole earth
C mi.

mf
sempre dim.
let the whole earth stand, let the whole
let the whole earth stand in awe of
Fmi.
stand in awe, let the whole earth
stand in awe, let the whole earth
sempre dim.
p rall.
earth stand in awe of Him.
Him, let the whole earth stand in awe of Him.
stand in awe of Him, in awe of Him.
stand in awe of Him.

Allegro energico

|| : | : | : | : | (m) .s :s .s |s : ||

CHORUS *ff*

|| : | : | : | : | (t,) .r :m .m |r : ||

The Lord is King,

|| : | : | : | : | (se) .t :d' .d' |t : ||

SOLO

|| Fmaj.3 d : (1) .d ,r |m .r :m ,f .s |m .d :s .s |s :–.fe | s .s :m .d |s : ||

CHORUS

Tell it out a-mong the heathen that the Lord is King, the Lord is King,

Allegro energico

f *ff*

|| .s :s .s |s : C t s .d' | t : | .t :d' .d | t : | : ||

|| .r :m .m |r : .r s | s : | .s :s .s | s : | : ||

the Lord is King, is King, the Lord is King:

|| .t :d' .d' |t : .t m' | r' : | .r' :m' .m' | r' : | : ||

|| .s :m .d |s : .s d | s : | .s :m .d | s : .l |d' .m ,s :d .d s ,f ||

mf SOLO fF

and that it is He that hath

mf

|| m .f ,s :l ,s .f ,m |f ,s .l ,f :s ,f .m ,r |m ,f .s ,m :f ,m .r ,d |r ,m .f ,r :m .r ,d |s :,s .s, |d .,r :r .,m ||

made the round ——————————— world so sure that it can-not be

CHORUS
'Tis He, 'tis He, 'tis He that hath made the
CHORUS
'Tis He, 'tis He, that hath made the round
CHORUS
'Tis He, 'tis He, that hath made the round
CHORUS
mov - ed! 'Tis He, 'tis He, 'tis He that hath made the round
CHORUS
round world so sure that it can-not be mov - 'ed;
world so sure that it can-not be mov - ed;
world so sure that it can-not, it can-not be mov - ed;
SOLO
world so sure that it can-not be mov-ed and how that He shall

judge the peo-ple righteously, and how that He shall judge, shall judge the people righteous-
CHORUS f
He shall judge the peo-ple righteous-ly, shall judge the peo-ple
f
-ly,
f
ff allargando
righteously, shall judge the peo - ple righ - teous - ly.
ff allargando
ff allargando

Allegretto moderato

SOLO *mp*

Al-le-lu - jah, Al -

SOLO *mp*

Al-le -

SOLO *mp*

Al-le-lu - jah, Al - le - lu-jah, Al-le-lu-jah, Al -

SOLO *mp*

Al-le-lu - jah, Al - le - lu-jah, Al-le-

Allegretto moderato

mp

- le-lu-jah, Al - le-lu - jah, Al-le-lu - jah,

mf CHORUS

-lu - jah, Al - le - lu-jah, Al-le - lu - jah, Al-le - lu-

mf CHORUS

-lu - jah, Al - le - lu - jah, Al-le-

CHORUS *mf*

-lu - jah, Al - le - lu - jah, Al-le - lu -

CHORUS *mf*

mf

8ves

N.B. *The organ interlude to be found in the Purcell Society edition may well be used.* [*Ed.*]

cresc.
Al-le-lu - jah, Al - le - lu - jah, Al - le-lu-jah, Al-
-jah, Al-le-lu - jah, Al-le-lu - jah, Al -
-lu - jah, Al - le-lu-jah, Al-le-lu - jah, Al -
-jah, Al - le - lu - jah, Al-le-lu - jah, Al - le -
Ped.
-le-lu - jah, Al-le-lu - jah, Al-le - lu-jah, Al -
-le - lu - jah, Al-le-lu - jah, Al-le -
-le - lu - jah, Al-le-lu - -
-lu - jah, Al-le-lu - jah, Al-le -
mf
8ves

cresc.
f
-le-lu - jah, Al-le-lu - jah, Al-le-lu - jah, Al - - le-lu-
cresc.
f
-lu - jah, Al-le-lu - jah, Al - le-lu -
cresc.
f
-jah, Al-le-lu - jah, Al-le - lu -
cresc.
f
-lu - jah, Al-le-lu - jah, Al-le-
cresc.
f
allargando
ff
-jah, Al-le-lu - jah, Al - - - le-lu - jah. A - men.
allargando
ff
- - jah, Al-le-lu - jah, Al-le - lu - jah. A - men.
allargando
ff
-jah, Al-le-lu-jah, Al-le-lu-jah, Al-le - lu - jah. A - men.
allargando
ff
-lu - jah, Al-le-lu - jah, Al-le - lu - jah. A - men.
allargando
ff
Ped.

20 ETERNAL FATHER

known, which is Love,— Till its loud prais-es sound at heaven's high
gate.
dim. e rit.
dim. e rit.
SOP.
p a tempo
ALTO
Per-fect Thy king-dom in our pass-ing state, That
p a tempo
TEN.
BASS
a tempo
p

here on earth Thou mayst as well ap-prove Our hom-age as Thou own-est
theirs a - bove___ Whose joy we ec-ho, and in pain a - wait.___
pp
(no Pedals)
SOLO SOPRANO
p meno mosso
Grant bo - dy and soul each day their dai - ly bread: And should in
meno mosso

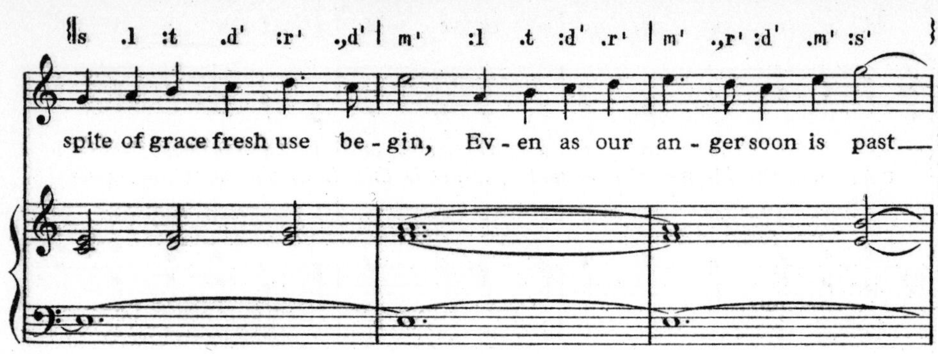
s .l :t .d' :r' .,d' | m' :l .t :d' .r' | m' .,r' :d' .m' :s'
spite of grace fresh use be - gin, Ev - en as our an - ger soon is past

— .d' :r' :— .m' | m' .r' :m' :l | d' :f :m .r | m :— :—
— and dead, Be Thy re-membrance mor - tal of our sin.

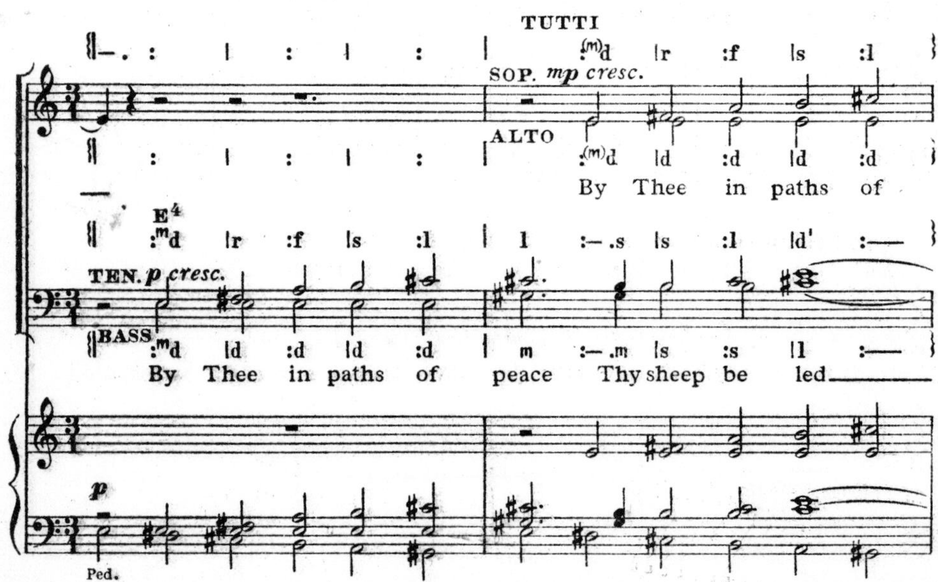
TUTTI
SOP. mp cresc.
ALTO
By Thee in paths of
E4
TEN. p cresc.
BASS
By Thee in paths of peace Thy sheep be led
p
Ped.

Tempo I

peace Thy sheep be led.

dim.

And in the vale of ter - ror com - fort - ed.

Tempo I

ppp

*SOP. I

Al - le - lu - ia, Al - le - lu -

*SOP. II

ppp

Al - le - lu - ia, Al - le - lu - ia,

*SOP. III

ppp

Al - le - lu - ia, Al - le - lu - ia,

TEN. & BASS

BELLS

pp (with soft felt striker)

ORGAN PEDALS

(sempre ppp)

*If possible these Sopranos should be placed far away.

If the Alleluias are found to be too difficult for choirs with limited resources, they may be filled in on the swell organ.

- ia, Al - le - lu - ia, Al - le - lu -
Al - le - lu - ia, Al - le - lu - ia,
Al - le - lu - ia, Al - le - lu - ia,
mp
E - ter - nal Fa - ther, who didst all cre -
- ia, Al - le - lu - ia, Al - le - lu -
Al - le - lu - ia, Al - le - lu - ia,
Al - le - lu - ia, Al - le - lu - ia,
- ate, In whom we live, and to whose bo - som

ia, Al - le - lu - ia, Al - le - lu -
Al - le - lu - ia, Al - le - lu - ia,
Al - le - lu - ia, Al - le - lu - ia,
move, To all men be Thy name known
- ia, Al - le - lu - ia, Al - le - lu -
Al - le - lu - ia, Al - le - lu - ia,
Al - le - lu - ia, Al - le - lu - ia,
which is Love, Till its loud prais - es

ia, Al-le-lu-ia, Al-le-lu-
Al-le-lu-ia, Al-le-lu-ia,
Al-le-lu-ia, Al-le-lu-ia,
dim.
sound at heaven's high gate.
-ia, Al-le-lu-ia, Al-le-lu-ia.
Al-le-lu-ia, Al-le-lu-ia, Al-le-lu-ia.
Al-le-lu-ia, Al-le-lu-ia, Al-le-lu-ia.
morendo
morendo

21 FROM ALL THAT DWELL BELOW THE SKIES

ISAAC WATTS
(1674–1748)

THOMAS ATTWOOD WALMISLEY
(1814–56)

This anthem may be sung unaccompanied. *The repeat is optional.*

D.C.
ev - 'ry tongue, Thro' ev - 'ry land by ev - 'ry tongue.
p (A FEW VOICES)
cresc.
E - ter - nal are Thy mer - cies, Lord, E - ter - nal truth at -
Thy mer - cies, Lord, E - ter - nal truth at -
- tends Thy word, E - ter - nal truth, E - ter -
- tends Thy word, E - ter - nal truth, E -
E - ter - nal truth,
Thy praise shall
CHORUS
- nal truth at - tends Thy word;
- ter - nal truth at - tends Thy word; Thy praise shall sound,
CHORUS
CHORUS
E - ter - nal truth at - tends Thy word; Thy praise shall sound,

sound from shore to shore, Thy praise shall sound from shore to
CHORUS
Thy praise shall sound Thy praise shall sound from shore to
Thy praise shall sound shall sound, Thy praise shall sound from shore to
Thy praise shall sound, shall sound from shore to
shore, Thy praise shall sound from shore to shore, shall sound from
cresc.
ff
shore, Till suns shall rise and
shore, Till suns shall rise and
shore, Till suns shall rise and
shore to shore, Till suns shall rise and set no
dim.
p
set, till suns shall rise and set no
set no more, till suns shall rise and set no
set, till suns shall rise and set no
more, till suns shall rise and set no more.
f
poco rit.
more, till suns shall rise and set, and set no more.
more, till suns shall rise and set no more.

22 GOD BE IN MY HEAD

Words from 'Sarum Primer' 1558 H. WALFORD DAVIES

To be sung unaccompanied.

23 GOD IS A SPIRIT

John IV. 24, 23

W. STERNDALE BENNETT
(1816–75)

This anthem may be sung unaccompanied

and they that wor-ship Him,
truth. God is a Spi-rit: God is a
must wor - ship Him, must wor - ship Him, in
Spi - rit: they must wor - ship Him, in
wor - ship Him, in
spi-rit and in truth: for the Fa - ther seek-eth
for the Fa - ther seeketh such,
such, seek - eth such, seek - eth such, seek - eth
seek - eth
cresc.

(FULL)
dim.
pp tranquillo assai
such to wor - ship Him. God is a Spi - rit,
cresc.
p
God is a Spi - rit, and they that wor - ship
and they
Him, they they that worship Him, must wor-ship Him, must
cresc.
f
wor-ship Him, and they that wor - ship Him, and

they that
must worship Him, must worship Him in
they that
p sempre calando
spirit and in truth: for the Father seeketh
such, for the Father seeketh such to
seek eth
pp rall.
worship Him, to worship Him, in spirit and in truth.
pp rall.

24 GOD SO LOVED THE WORLD

This Anthem may be sung unaccompanied.

have ev-er-last - ing life. For God sent not His
have ev-er-last-ing life. For God sent not His
have ev-er-last - ing life. For God sent not His
have ev-er-last-ing life. For God sent not His
Son in-to the world to con-demn the world;
cresc.
but that the world through Him, through Him might be
cresc.
sa - - ved. A - - - - - - men.
A - - - - - - - men.

25 GRANT US THY PEACE

MOTET FOR FOUR VOICES

F. MENDELSSOHN-BARTHOLDY
(1809–47)

Originally written with accompaniment for strings.

cresc.
ev - 'ry_ bless - ing! We can-not keep
cresc.
dim.
Thy sav-ing Word, Un-less Thy peace pos-sess - -
dim.
dolce
-ing. Thy peace O give by
p cresc.
sf
which we live.
dim.

SOPRANO (SOLO or FULL)
p dolce
Grant us Thy peace, Al - might - y Lord, O source of
BASS p
O grant us Thy peace, Al -
sf
ev - 'ry bless - ing! We can - not keep
- might - y Lord! We can - not keep Thy sav - ing
cresc.
Thy sav - ing word, Un - less Thy peace pos - sess -
word, We can - not keep Un - less Thy
cresc.
dim.
F

cresc.
-ing, Thy peace O give by
cresc.
peace po - sess - ing, Thy peace O give
p cresc. sf p
which we live.
by which we live.
p cresc.
(SOLI or CHORUS) SOPRANO mf
ALTO
Grant us Thy peace, Al-
TENOR mf
BASS
f mf

-might - y Lord! O Source of ev - 'ry bless -
-ing, We can-not keep Thy sav-ing word,
Un-less Thy peace pos-sess - ing,
Un-less Thy peace pos-sess - ing, peace po-sess - ing.
Al -
dim.
p
cresc.

Thy peace O give, by
cresc.
cresc
Thy peace O give, O give, by
Thy peace O give Thy peace O give, by
cresc.
-might - y Lord! Thy peace O give, by
cresc.
sf
cresc
sf
Cmi.t
dim.
dim.
which we live, Thy peace O give, by which we
which we live, Thy peace O give, by
dim.
dim.
dim.
live.
which we live.
dim.
pp

26 HARK, THE GLAD SOUND!

PHILLIP DODDRIDGE (1702-51) — H. WALFORD DAVIES

throne, And ev- ery voice a song!
dim.
Org. Ped. ad lib.

|m :r |s :t,.s |s :—.d |l :s |m .f :r |d :de se |l :t .d' }

|m :r |s :t,.t, |d :—.d |d :d |d :t, |l, :l m |m :f .m }

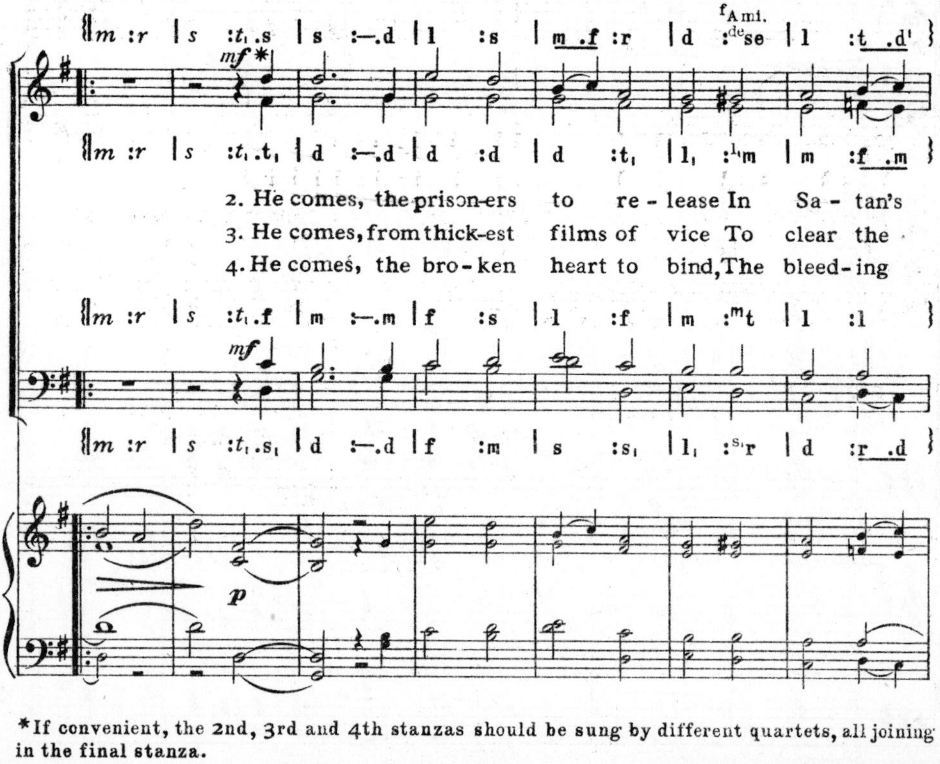

2. He comes, the prison-ers to re - lease In Sa - tan's
3. He comes, from thick-est films of vice To clear the
4. He comes, the bro - ken heart to bind, The bleed - ing

|m :r |s :t,.f |m :—.m |f :s |l :f |m :m t |l :l }

|m :r |s :t,.s, |d :—.d |f :m |s :s, |l, :s r |d :r .d }

*If convenient, the 2nd, 3rd and 4th stanzas should be sung by different quartets, all joining in the final stanza.

2. bond-age held; The gates of brass be - fore Him
3. men - tal ray, And on the eye - balls of the
4. soul to cure, And with the trea - sures of His
2. bond-age held; The gates of brass be - fore Him
3. men - tal ray, And on the eye-balls of the
4. soul to cure, And with the trea-sures of His
2. bond-age held; The gates of brass be - fore Him
3. men - tal ray, And on the eye - balls of the
4. soul to cure, And with the trea - sures of His
2. bond-age held; The gates of brass be - fore Him
3. men - tal ray, And on the eye - - - balls of the
4. soul to cure, And with the trea - - - sures of His
2. burst, The i - ron fet-ters yield.
3. blind To pour ce - les-tial day.
4. grace To en-rich the hum-ble poor.
p
p
mf
p

f A mi.

|m.r :s .t |m'.r' :s |s :— .d |l :s |m .f :r |d :de se

ff

| : | :s, |s, :— .d |l, :s, |m .f :r |d :de se

5. Our glad Ho-san-nas, Prince of Peace, Thy

| : | :s |s :— .d |l :s |m .f :r |d :de se

ff

| : | :s :s, |s :— .d |l :s |m .f :r |d :de se

cresc. *ff*

lunga
arch-es ring With Thy be - lov-ed Name. A - men.
lunga
dim.

A Hymn Tune Version for Congregational use

Key G
A mi.

27 HE IS BLESSED THAT COMETH

BENEDICTUS from REQUIEM

Matt. xxi. 9.

WOLFGANG AMADEUS MOZART
(1756-91)
Edited by EDWARD J. DENT

Andante

(From Mozart's Requiem. O.U.P. edition)

SOLO
TUTTI
Lord He is bless - ed that
He is bless-ed, is bless - ed that comes in the name of the
He is bless-ed that
He is bless - ed that com - eth,
com - eth He is bless - ed that com - eth, that
Lord, He is bless - ed that com - - eth, that
com-eth He is bless - ed, is
that comes in the name of the Lord, He is bless - ed, is

com - - eth in the name of the Lord, He is bless-ed
com - - eth in the name of the Lord, He is bless-ed
bless - ed that com - eth in the name of the Lord, He is
bless - ed that com - eth in the name of the Lord, He is
that com - eth, that com - eth, that com-eth in the
that com - eth, is bless - ed that com-eth in the
bless - ed that com - eth, is bless - ed that com-eth in the
bless - ed that com - eth, is bless - ed that com-eth in the

name of the Lord!
name of the Lord!
name of the Lord!
name of the Lord!
Wind
Str.
Wind
Str.
Wind
ff
He is
He is
He is
He is bless-ed
TUTTI
p
V'Cello
Str. & W.W.
mf

bless-ed that com-eth, that
bless-ed that com-eth, that
bless-ed that com-eth, that
f Bb
that com-eth, that com - eth in the
com - eth in the name of the Lord!
com - eth in the name of the Lord!
com - eth in the name of the Lord!
name of the Lord!
Vln.
p sf
Fag. sf p sf

BASS
He is bless-ed, is bless-ed that com-eth in the
Str.
p
TEN.
He is bless-ed, is bless-ed that
BASS
name of the Lord!
SOP.
He is bless-ed that
ALTO
He is bless - ed
TEN.
com-eth in the name of the Lord!

com-eth, that com - eth in the name of the
that com - eth, that com - eth, that
He is bless-ed that com - eth, is bless - ed that
He is bless - ed that com - eth, is
Lord, that com-eth in the name, in the name of the
com - eth in the name, that com-eth in the name of the
com - eth in the name, that com-eth in the name of the
bless - ed that com - eth in the name of the
cresc.

Lord, He is bless - ed that
Lord, He is bless - ed that com - eth,
Lord, He is bless - ed that com - eth,
Lord, He is bless-ed that
fp L.H. pp W.W.
com - eth, He is bless - ed that com - eth, that
that comes in the name — of the Lord, is bless - ed that
that comes in the name — of the Lord, He is bless - ed that
com-eth is bless - ed that com-eth, He is bless - ed that

com - eth in_ the_ name of the Lord, He is bless-ed
com - - eth in the name of the Lord, He is
com - eth, that com-eth in_ the_ name of the Lord, He is
com - eth, that com - eth in the name of the Lord, He is bless-ed
Str.
that ___ com ___ eth is bless - ed He that com-eth in_ the_
bless - ed that com - eth, that com-eth in the name, in the
bless - ed that com - eth, that com-eth in the name, in the
is bless - ed that com-eth in the

name of the Lord, He is bless-ed that com-eth, is
name of the Lord, He is bless-ed that com-eth, is
name of the Lord, He is bless-ed that com-eth, that com-eth,
name of the Lord, He is bless-ed that com-eth, that com-eth,
Trombs.
bless - ed that com - eth, that com - eth in the name of the
dol.
bless - ed that com - eth, that com-eth in the name of the
is bless-ed that com-eth in the name, in the name of the
is bless-ed that com-eth in the name, in the name of the
dim.

Lord.
Lord.
Lord.
Lord.
Vlns.
ff Wind
Str.
Wind
Str.
Wind
Fag.
TUTTI L.H.
Allegro
CHORUS
Ho - san-na in the high -
Allegro
L.H.

CHORUS
Ho -
CHORUS
Ho - - san-na in the high - - - -
- - - - est, Ho - san - na in the high - -
-san - na in the high - - - - -
est, Ho - san - na in the high - - -
- - - - est, in the high - - - - - - -
CHORUS
Ho -

est, Ho - san - - na in the high - - - est,
- - est, Ho - san - - na in the high - est,
- - - - est, Ho - san - na -
-san - na in the high - - - - - -
Ho - - san - na in the high - - est!
Ho - - san - na in the high - - est!
in the high - est, in the high - - est!
-est, Ho - san - na in the high - - est!
Trpts.

NOTE: The Hosanna Chorus may well be sung twice. [*Ed.*]

28 HE THAT SHALL ENDURE TO THE END

Chorus from 'ELIJAH' Matt. xxiv 13

FELIX MENDELSSOHN BARTHOLDY (1809-47)

cresc.
dim.
sa - ved, shall be sa - - - ved,
f
dim.
ved, he that shall en - dure to the end,
dim.
shall be sa - ved, shall be
be sa - ved,
cresc.
f
dim.
p
cresc.
shall be sa - ved, shall be sa - ved,
p
cresc.
shall be sa - ved, sa - ved,
p
cresc.
sa - ved, shall be, shall be sa - ved,
cresc.
f
he that shall en dure to the end, shall
p
cresc.

A mi.
dim.
p
cresc.
shall — be sa - ved, he that shall en - dure to the
he that shall en-dure to the end, — that
shall — be sa - ved, he that shall en - dure to the end —
— be sa - - ved, he that
f
D mi.
end shall — be sa - ved,
shall en-dure to the end shall be — sa - - ved; — he that
— shall — be sa - ved, he that shall en -
shall en-dure to the end shall be sa - ved; he that shall en-dure to the end —

‖s :s |s :m |l :s .f |m :— |f :s |l :d' |ta :— |l :— |s :l |t :r'

cresc. sf f dim -

he that shall en - dure to the end shall — be sa - ved, shall —

‖r :d .t, |d :— |— :d .t, |d :d |— :d |— :d |r :m |f :l |r :— |s :r

f

shall en - dure — to the end he — shall be sa - ved, shall be —

‖t :s .f |s :s |— .f :m .r |d :l |— :m |f :— | : | : |t :d' |r' :t

f dim -

-dure to the end shall — be — sa - ved; shall —

‖— :m .r |m :d |f, :s, |l, :— |l, :d |f :l |s :— |f :— |— :— | . :

f

— shall be sa - ved, shall — be sa - ved, —

f p dim -

‖d' :— |t :— |l :— |s :— |d :r |m :s |f :— |m :— |l, :t, |d :m |r :— |— :— |d :— |— :—‖

-in - u - en - do p pp

— be sa - ved, shall — be sa - ved, shall — be sa - ved.

‖m :r |— :s |— :f |— :m |l, :t, |d :m |r :— |d :— |l, :— |— :d |d :— |t, :— |s, :— |— :—‖

p pp

sa - - ved, shall — be sa - ved, shall be sa - ved.

‖s :l |— :s |l :t |— :d' |l :— |s :— | : |l :— |— :— |— :l |l :— |s :f |m :— |— :—‖

-in - u - en - do p pp

— be sa - ved, shall — be sa - ved.

‖m, :f, |s, :t, |d :r |m :s |f :— |m :— | : | : |l, :— |— :s, |f, :— |s, :— |d, :— |— :—‖

dim. p pp

shall — be sa - ved, shall be sa - ved.

-in - u - en - do p dim. pp

29 HEAR, LORD. LORD, MAKE HASTE TO HELP US

PETER ILICH TCHAIKOVSKY
(1840-93)

The pauses must never break the sense or continuity of this anthem.

Un-to Thee we cry.
There is none to aid us-
unis.
dim.
Hear Thy peo-ple's cry;
Turn a-way Thine an-ger;
sempre dim.
p

Fm.t

‖s .s :s .s |s :— |— :𝄐 |s :s |^{l}r :r |m :— }

pp *cresc.*

‖m .m :m .m |m :— |— :𝄐 |s :s |^{l}r :r |m :— }

Hear Thy peo-ple's cry.______ Show Thy lov - ing kind -

‖d .d :d .d |d :— |— :𝄐 |m :m |^{m}l, :l, |se, :— }

mp unis. *cresc.*

Hear Thy peo-ple's cry.______ Show Thy lov - ing kind -

‖s .s :s .s |s :— |— :𝄐 |m :m |^{m}l, :l, |t, :— }

pp *cresc.*

‖m .m :m .m |m :— |— :𝄐 |m :m |^{m}l, :l, |t, :— }

Hear Thy peo-ple's cry.______ Show Thy lov - ing kind -

‖d .d :d .d |d :— |— :𝄐 |d :d |^{d}f, :f, |m, :— }

mp *cresc.*

Hear Thy peo-ple's cry.______ Show Thy lov - ing kind -

cresc.

E♭t fA♭

‖d :𝄐 |^{m}l :l |t :t |d' :— |l :𝄐 |$^{d'}$s .s :s .s }

sempre cresc. *f*

‖d :𝄐 |^{m}l :l |t :t |d' :— |l :𝄐 |^{l}m .m :m .m }

- ness; Rise up for our help, Lord. Hear Thy peo-ple's

‖l, :𝄐 |^{d}f :f |f :f |m :— |f :𝄐 |^{f}d .d :d .d }

sempre cresc. *f*

- ness; Rise up for our help, Lord. Hear Thy peo-ple's

‖m :𝄐 |^{d}f :f |s :s |s :— |d' :𝄐 |$^{d'}$s .s :s .s }

sempre cresc. *f*

‖m :𝄐 |^{d}f :f |s :s |s :— |d' :𝄐 |^{l}m .m :m .m }

- ness; Rise up for our help, Lord. Hear Thy peo-ple's

‖l, :𝄐 |^{l}r :r |r :r |d :— |f :𝄐 |^{f}d .d :d .d }

sempre cresc. *f*

- ness; Rise up for our help, Lord. Hear Thy peo-ple's

sempre cresc. *f*

cry. Plen-te-ous in mer - cy, Grant us Thy sal-
cry. Plen-te-ous in mer - cy, Grant us Thy sal-
cry. Plen-te-ous in mer - cy, Grant us Thy sal-
cry. Plen-te-ous in mer - cy, Grant us Thy sal-
Slightly slower
- va - tion; O Lord, hear our cry. A - men.
unis.
- va - tion; O Lord, hear our cry. A - men.
- va - tion; O Lord, hear our cry. A - men.
- va - tion; O Lord, hear our cry. A - men.
Slightly slower

30 HIDE NOT THOU THY FACE FROM US O LORD

From Bernards 'First Book of Cathedral Musicke' (1641)

RICHARD FARRANT
d. 1580

Edited by A. RAMSBOTHAM

♩= about 108

Key F mi.

SOP. ALTO TEN. BASS

O Lord,
Hide not Thou Thy face from us, O Lord, and

dis-plea - - sure:
cast not off Thy ser - vant in Thy dis - plea - sure:

un - - to Thee, and hide not
for we con - fess our sins un - to Thee, and hide not

our un-right - e-ous - ness: for thy mer - cy sake, for Thy
— our unright - eous - ness: for Thy mer - cy sake, for Thy
our un-right - e - ous - ness: for Thy mer - cy sake, for Thy

Original: a minor third lower

This anthem may be sung unaccompanied. Reprinted by permission from the Tudor Church Music Series (Oxford University Press.)

mf
mer - cy sake de - liv - er us from all our sins, de -
mf
(pp)
all our sins:
-liv - er us from all our sins: for Thy
(pp)
-liv-er us from all our sins:
mer - cy sake, for Thy mer - cy sake de - liv - er us from
rall.
all our sins.
all our sins, de - liv - er us from all our sins.
rall.
all our sins, de - liv-er us from all our sins.

31

HOLY, HOLY, HOLY

(SANCTUS)

Translated from the German by
CHRISTINA CUMMING CAIRNS

FRANZ SCHUBERT
from the German Mass II, 1826
(1797–1828)

G This anthem may be sung unaccompanied.

32 HOLY, HOLY, HOLY

REGINALD HEBER (1783-1826) | PETER ILICH TCHAIKOVSKY (1840-93)

This Anthem may be sung unaccompanied.

mf
dim.
Ho - ly! Mer-ci-ful and Might - y, God in Three
Ho - ly! Mer-ci - ful and Mighty, God in Three
Ho - ly! Mer-ci - ful and Mighty, God in Three
Ho-ly Ho - ly! Mer-ci - ful and Mighty, God in Three
p
pp
Per-sons, bless-ed Trin - i - ty. Ho-ly, Ho-ly,
Per-sons, bless-ed Trin - i - ty. Ho - ly, Ho - ly,
Per-sons, bless-ed Trin - i - ty. Ho - ly, Ho - ly,
Per - sons, bless-ed Trin - i - ty. Ho - ly, Ho - ly,

Ho - ly! All the saints a - dore Thee, Cast - ing down their
Ho - ly! All the saints a - dore Thee, Cast - ing down their
Ho - ly! All the saints a - dore Thee, Cast - ing down their
Ho - ly! All the saints a - dore Thee, Cast - ing down their
gold - en crowns a - round the glass - y sea; Cher - u - bim and
gold - en crowns a - round the glass - y sea; Cher - u -
gold - en crowns a - round the glass - y sea; Cher - u -
gold - en crowns a - round the glass - y sea; Cher - u -
cresc.

ser - a - phim fall-ing down be - fore Thee, Which wert and
-bim fall-ing down be - fore Thee, Which wert and
-bim fall-ing down be - fore Thee, Which wert and
-bim and ser - a - phim fall-ing down be - fore Thee, Which wert and
f
dim.
art, and ev - er - more shalt be. Ho - ly, Ho - ly,
art, and ev - er - more shalt be. Ho - ly, Ho - ly,
art, and ev - er - more shalt be. Ho - ly, Ho - ly,
art, and ev - er - more shalt be. Ho - ly, Ho - ly,
mp
p

Ho - ly! Though the dark-ness hide Thee, Though the eye of
Ho - ly! Though the dark-ness hide Thee, Though the eye of
Ho - ly! Though the dark-ness hide Thee, Though the eye of
Ho - ly! Though the dark-ness hide Thee, Though the eye of
sin-ful man Thy glo-ry may not see, On - ly Thou art
sin-ful man Thy glo-ry may not see, On - ly
sin-ful man Thy glo-ry may not see, On - ly
sin-ful man Thy glo-ry may not see, On - ly

cresc.
Ho - ly, There is none be - side Thee Per - fect
Thou, There is none be-side Thee Per - fect
Thou, There is none be-side Thee Per - fect
Thou art Ho - ly There is none be-side Thee Per - fect
in pow-er, in love, and pur - i - ty.
in pow-er, in love, and pur - i - ty.
in pow-er, in love, and pur - i - ty.
in pow-er, in love, and pur - i - ty.

Più mosso
mf
Ho - ly, Ho - ly, Ho - ly! Lord God Al - might - y!
Ho - ly, Ho - ly, Ho - ly! Lord God Al - might - y!
Ho - ly, Ho - ly, Ho - ly! Lord God Al - might - y!
Ho - ly, Ho - ly, Ho - ly! Lord God Al - might - y!
Più mosso
mf
All Thy works shall praise Thy Name in earth and sky and sea:
All Thy works shall praise Thy Name in earth and sky and sea:
All Thy works shall praise Thy Name in earth and sky and sea:
All Thy works shall praise Thy Name in earth and sky and sea:

|l, :t, |d :r |f :m.f |r : |m :f |s :l |d' :t.d' |l :s |

cresc.

Ho - ly, Ho - ly, Ho - ly! Mer - ci - ful and Might - y!

| : |d :t, |l, :— |s, : | : |s :f |m.f :s |f :m |

cresc.

Ho - ly, Ho - ly! Mer - ci - ful and Might - y!

| : |l, :t, |d :—.r |t, : | : |m :f |s :s |d' :t.d' |

cresc.

Ho - ly, Ho - ly! Mer - ci - ful and Might - y!

| : |l, :s, |f, :l,.r, |s, :l,.t, |d : |m :r |d :m, |f, :s, |

cresc.

Ho - ly, Ho - ly, Ho - ly! Mer - ci - ful and Might - y!

cresc.

|f :— |m :r.d |r :— |r : | : | : | : | : |

God in Three Per - sons,

|r :s,.l, |s, :f,.l, |l, :— |l, : |r :d |f :m |r :d |r :m.r |

f

God in Three Per - sons, Hal - le - lu - jah!

|l :r' |d' :l.m |r :— |r : | : | : | : | : |

God in Three Per - sons,

|l, :t, |d :r.l, |f, :— |f, : | : |r :d |f :m |r :d.t, |

f

God in Three Per - sons, Hal - le - lu -

G2

N.B. When this anthem is sung by a small choir, it may be well to make a diminuendo in the last four bars, ending *pp*.

33 I HEARD A VOICE FROM HEAVEN

Rev. xiv, 13.

JOHN GOSS
(1800-80)

This Anthem may be sung unaccompanied.

in the Lord, Bless - ed are the dead which die in the
Lord: E - ven so, saith the Spi-rit; E - ven
so, saith the Spi-rit; for they rest from their la-bours, they

* This may be sung by a single voice.

Bless -
dol.
rest, they rest from their la - - bours.
dol.
dol.
- ed, bless - ed are the dead which die in the
Bless - ed are the dead which die in the
Ped
Lord, for they rest from their la - bours.
slower
dim.
Lord, for they rest, they rest from their la - bours.
slower
dim.
Lord, for they rest from their la - bours.
slower
dim.

34 I KNOW THAT MY REDEEMER LIVES

Job xix, 25.26 and part 27

JOH. MICHAEL BACH (1648-94)

* The compass of the Alto part is such that it can be sung by Sopranos. This anthem may be sung unaccompanied.

stand, He shall stand at the last up - on the Earth:
stand, He shall stand at the last up - on the Earth:
stand, He shall stand at the last up - on the Earth:
stand, He shall stand at the last up - on the Earth:
And though af - ter my skin worms destroy, de - stroy my bo -
And though af - ter my skin worms — de - stroy my bo -
And though af - ter my skin worms destroy, de - stroy my bo -
And though af - ter my skin worms de - stroy my bo -

(CHORAL: CHRISTUS DER IST MEIN LEBEN)

Christ is my Life e - ter - -
- dy; Yet in my flesh shall I see God, shall I see God,
- dy; Yet in my flesh shall I see God, shall I see God,
- dy; Yet in my flesh shall I see God, shall I see God,
- dy; Yet in my flesh shall I see God, shall I see God,
- nal And death to me is
see God, in my flesh shall I see God, see God; whom
in my flesh shall I, shall I see God; whom
and in my flesh shall I see God; whom
and in my flesh shall I see God; whom

gain. With joy my
I shall see for my-self, see for my-self, see for my-
I shall see for my-self, see for my-self, see for my-
I shall see for my-self, see for my-self, see for my-
I shall see for my-self, see for my-self, see for my-
spi - rit yield - - ing
-self, whom I shall see for my-self and mine
-self, whom I shall see, shall see for myself and mine
-self, whom I shall see, shall see for my-self and mine
-self, whom I shall see, shall see for my-self and mine

I rise with
eyes shall be-hold, shall be-hold, and not an-o-ther; whom
eyes shall be-hold, shall be-hold, and not an-o-ther; whom
eyes shall be-hold, shall be-hold, and not an-o-ther; whom
eyes shall be-hold, shall be-hold, and not an-o-ther; whom
dim. e rall.
Him and reign.
I shall see for my-self, and not an-o-ther.
I shall see for my-self, and not an-o-ther.
I shall see for my-self, and not an-o-ther.
I shall see for my-self, and not an-o-ther.
p

35 IF WE BELIEVE THAT JESUS DIED

1 Thess. iv. 14, 18

JOHN GOSS
(1800-80)

mf
If
f Dmi.
mf
If we be-lieve that Je - sus died and rose a -
- gain, and rose a - gain, If we be-lieve that Je - sus
we be-lieve that Je - sus died and rose a - gain,
we be-lieve that Je - sus died and rose a -
cresc.
gain, If we be-lieve that Je-sus died and rose a -
cresc.
died and rose a-gain, be - lieve that Je-sus died and rose a -
cresc.
If we be-lieve that Je - sus rose a -
cresc.

-gain, ev'n so them al-so which sleep in Je-sus,
-gain, ev'n so them al-so which sleep in Je - sus,
-gain, ev'n so them al-so which sleep in Je-sus, which
-gain, ev'n so them al-so which sleep in Je-sus,
which sleep in Je - sus, will God bring with Him will
which sleep in Je - sus, will God bring with
sleep in Je - sus,
sleep in Je - sus, will God
cres - cen - do
cresc.

SOPRANO I
God, will God bring with Him, will
SOPRANO II
God bring, will God bring with Him, will,
Him, will God bring with Him,
will God, will God bring, will God
bring with Him, will God bring with Him, will
Unis
God bring with Him. If we be-
will God bring with Him. If
bring with Him.
God bring with with Him. If
mf

-lieve that Je - sus died, if we be -
we be - lieve, if we be - lieve that
If we be - lieve that Je - sus
we be - lieve that Je - sus died, if we be -
-lieve that Je-sus died, that Je - sus died and
Je - sus died, that Je - sus died and
died, that Je-sus died and rose,
- lieve that Je - sus died, if we be-lieve that Je - sus

Dmaj.3
rose, and rose a - gain, ev'n so them
rose a - gain, ev'n so them
and rose a - gain, ev'n so them
rose a - gain, ev'n so them
al-so which sleep in Je - sus, which sleep in
al - so which sleep in Je - sus, which sleep in
al-so which sleep in Je - sus, which sleep in
al-so which sleep in Je - sus, sleep in

cres - cen - do
Je - sus, will God bring with Him, will God,
Je - sus, will God bring with Him, will
cres - cen - do
Je - - - sus, will God bring with
Je - sus, will God,
cres - cen - do
will God bring with Him, will
God bring with Him, will
Him, will God bring with Him, will God
will God bring with Him, will God

God bring with Him, will God bring with
God bring with Him, will God bring with
bring, will God bring with
bring with Him, will God bring with
Slow (𝅗𝅥=56)
Him. Where-fore com-fort one an-o-ther with these words.
Him. Where-fore com-fort one an-o-ther with these words.
Him. Where-fore com-fort one an-o-ther with these words.
Him. Where-fore com-fort one an-o-ther with these words.
Slow (𝅗𝅥=56)

36 IF YE LOVE ME

St. John XIV, 15, 16

THOMAS TALLIS
(1510–85)
Edited by A. RAMSBOTHAM

= about 100
Key F
SOPRANO
ALTO
TENOR
(8ve lower)
BASS
(for rehearsal)
If ye love me, keep my com-mand-ments, and I will
If ye love me, keep my com-mand-ments,
If ye love me, keep my com-mand-ments, and
If ye love me, keep my com-mand-ments,
pray the Fa - ther, and He shall
and I will pray the Fa - ther, and
I will pray the Fa - ther, and
and I will pray the Fa - ther,

From the Tudor Church Music Series (Oxford University Press) reprinted by permission.

In this Anthem (originally written for men's voices) the word 'Spirit' must be pronounced with a very short first syllable. In the time of Tallis the word was pronounced as one syllable.

This anthem may be sung unaccompanied.

give you an-o-ther Com-fort-er,
He shall give you an-o-ther Com - fort-er, that
He shall give you an-o - ther Com-fort-er, that He may
and He shall give you an o-ther Com-fort-er, that He
that He may bide with you for ev
He may bide with you for ev - er, with you for ev -
bide with you for ev - er, that He may bide with you for ev -
may bide with you for ev - er, may bide with you for ev -

1st SOP.
-er: Ev'n the Spirit of
-er: Ev'n the Spirit of truth, ev'n the
-er: Ev'n the Spirit of truth, the Spirit of truth,
-er: Ev'n the Spirit of truth, the Spirit of
Ev'n the Spirit of truth,
2nd SOP.
truth, ev'n the Spirit of truth, ev'n the Spirit of truth.
Spirit of truth, ev'n the Spirit of truth.
ev'n the Spirit of truth, the Spirit of truth, the Spirit of truth.
truth, ev'n the Spirit of truth, the Spirit of truth.

37
INTO THIS WORLD OF SORROW
(THE RENUNCIATION)
PERCY C. BUCK
Reprinted by permission
Non troppo lento (about 𝅗𝅥. = 34)
Key D mi.
SOP.
ALTO
TEN.
BASS
1. Into this world of sorrow,
2. Now is the time of His coming,
1. Into this valley of rue and sadness, Came
2. Now are our hearts with joy replete; But,
1. Christ our dear Consoler,
2. to lead men to Heaven,
1. And brought men gladness.
2. He bread of tears did eat.
1. And brought men gladness.
2. He bread of tears did eat.
1. And brought men gladness.
2. He bread of tears did eat.
This anthem may be sung unaccompanied.

38 IS IT NOTHING TO YOU?

Lamentations i. 12

FREDERICK A. GORE OUSELEY (1825-1889)

Very slow (𝅗𝅥 = 50)
D mi.
SOP. pp
ALTO
TEN. pp
BASS
that pass
Is it noth-ing to you, all ye that pass
pass
by? is it noth- ing to you, all ye that
cresc.
by? by?
is it noth- ing to you, all ye
pass by?
all
that pass by?
that pass by? Be-hold, and see, be-hold and see
ye that pass by?
sor - row
if there be a - ny sor - row like un-to My
sor - row

This anthem may be sung unaccompanied.

sor - row, if there be a - ny sor - row like
sor - row,
un-to My sor - row, which is done un-to
Me, which is done un-to Me, wherewith the Lord hath af - flict - ed
un - to
fierce an - - - ger.
Me in the day of His fierce an - - ger.
fierce an - - - ger.
fierce an - ger.
rall.
pp
mp
ppp

39 JESU, JOY AND TREASURE

I— [CHORALE] Verse I

Translated from the German by CHARLES SANFORD TERRY

JOHANN SEBASTIAN BACH (1685-1750)

Edited by W. GILLIES WHITTAKER

Key E mi.
SOP.
ALTO
TEN.
BASS
1 Je - su Joy and Treas - ure, So - lace pass - ing meas - ure, Pre - cious gift to me!
2 Long, so long I lan - guish, Torn my heart with an - guish Yearn-ing, Lord, for Thee.
Thine I am, O spot - less Lamb, In Thine arms I'd ever hide me; Earth holds nought be - side Thee.

To be sung unaccompanied.

H

39a

V— [CHORALE] Verse 3

Moderato
Key A mi.
SOP. I
SOP. II
ALTO
TEN.
BASS
Hence! hence! thou noi - some ser - - pent! Hence! thou noisome
ser-pent! Hence! hence! I mock Death's tor - - -
- ment, Hence! I mock Death's tor-ment. Bow in fear thy
- ment, Hence! I mock Death's tor-ment. Bow in fear thy
in fear thy

NOTE: The temporary substitution of $\frac{2}{4}$ for $\frac{3}{2}$ is indicated by dotted bar-lines.

crest! Bow in fear, bow in fear, bow in
crest! Bow, bow, bow,
crest!
fear, bow in fear thy crest! Rage ye,
bow in fear thy crest! Rage ye,
bow in fear, bow in fear thy crest! Rage ye,
Rage
A mi.
rage ye, rage ye, World, wild leap
rage ye, rage ye, World, wild leap
wild leap - ing!
ye, World, wild leap
E mi.
cresc.
ff
mf

‖l :l₁ .t₁ :d .l₁ |m .m₁ :m : |ba :— :se | .m :l :se .l ‖

p *cresc. molto*

‖l :l₁ t₁ :d l₁ |m m :t₁ : |r :— :r | m :m :— ‖

-ing! Rage ye, World, wild leaping! I stand here, and sing- - -

‖d :l₁ .t₁ :d .l₁ |m .m₁ :se₁ : |l₁ :— :t₁ | .se₁ l₁ :t₁ .d ‖

p *cresc. molto*

-ing! Rage ye, World, wild leaping! I stand here, and sing- - - -

‖— :l₁ .t₁ :d .l₁ |m .m :m : |r :— :f | .t :m :r .m ‖

p *cresc. molto*

‖l₁ :l₁ .t₁ :d .l₁ |m .m₁ :r : |d :— :t₁ | .r :d :t₁ .l₁ ‖

Calm in

‖se :m .ba :se .m |l .l₁ :l :— |— :l :— ‖

ff

‖m :m .ba :se .m |l l₁ :l :s |f :m :— ‖

-ing, I stand here, and sing-ing, Calm in peace, at

‖t₁ :m .ba :se .m |l .l₁ : :m |r :d :de ‖

ff *f*

-ing, I stand here, and sing-ing, in peace,— in

Calm in

‖m :m .ba :se .m |l l₁ : : | :l :s ‖

ff *f*

‖m :m .ba :se m |l l₁ : : | : : ‖

peace, at rest,

‖l .t :d' :— |— .t :se :— |l :s : .s |s .f :f :— ‖

dim. [*p*] *dim.*

‖r :m :l .s |f :m :r |d :de : .m |m .r :r :— ‖

rest, Calm in— peace,— at rest, Calm in peace, at rest, ———

‖r :d .t₁ :l₁ |r :t₁ :— |l₁ :m :r |de :r :d ‖

dim. [*p*]

peace, Calm in peace, at rest

peace, ——— and at rest Calm in peace,— at

‖f :m :f | :t₁ :m |m :l :t |m :f .s :l ‖

dim. [*p*]

mf [*p*]

‖ :l₁ .s₁ :f₁ .m₁ |r₁ :m₁ :— |l₁ :— :— |— :— :— ‖

Calm in peace, at rest, ———

NOTE: **The crotchet rest between 'I' and 'stand' occurs in the original.**

Calm in peace, at rest, Calm in peace,
rest, Calm in peace, at rest, Calm in
Calm in
at rest. 'Tis God's
peace, at rest, Calm in peace, at rest.
arm holds me from harm, 'Tis God's
'Tis God's arm holds me from harm, 'Tis God's
'Tis God's arm holds me from harm, 'Tis God's
'Tis God's arm holds me from harm, 'Tis God's

arm holds me from harm,
arm holds me from harm, Earth and
arm holds me from harm,
arm holds me from harm, Earth and
arm holds me from harm,
Ha - des, Earth and Ha - des rouse no
Ha - des, Earth and Ha - des rouse no
Ha - des rouse no ter-ror, Earth and Hades rouse no ter -
ter - ror, no ter - ror, Earth and Ha - des,
ter - ror, no ter - ror, Earth and Ha - des
- ror, Earth and Ha - des rouse no

no ter - ror, Though in wrath they
no ter - ror, Though in wrath they
ter - - - ror,
mut - - - - - - - - - - - - - - -
mut - - - - - - - - - - - - - - -
- - - - - ter, Though in wrath they mut - - ter.
- - ter, Though in wrath they mut - - ter.
- ter, Though in wrath they mut - - ter.
- - - ter, Though in wrath they mut - - ter.
dim.
A mi.
E mi.
B mi.

39b

XI—[CHORALE] Verse 6

Key F mi.
SOP.
ALTO
TEN.
BASS
mf
cresc.
ff
dim.
Ban - ish fear and sad - ness Come, sweet Lord of
Glad - ness, Je - su, Mas - ter mine!
Who do tru - ly serve Thee, Must by faith de -

cresc.
- serve Thee, Joy - ous bear Thy
sign. Scorn and hate may be man's fate;
Lit - tle worth in them I meas -
- ure, Je - su, Joy and treas - ure!
dim. e rall.
ppp

40 JESU, JOY OF MAN'S DESIRING

From CHURCH CANTATA No. 147

'Herz und Mund und That und Leben'

English Translation from Church Music Society's Reprints *by permission*

Arranged by JOHANN SEBASTIAN BACH (1685-1750) *on a chorale by JOHANN SHOP (d. 1666)*
Edited by W. GILLIES WHITTAKER

*NOTE: ♩. ♪ must be interpreted as ♩ ♪ (triplet) throughout, and very lightly played.
For organ accompaniment see Church Music Society's Reprint No. 16a.
Expression marks in brackets refer to repeat.

man's de - sir - ing,
Hope is guid - ing,
cresc. Ho - ly
dim. Hark, what
cresc.
(dim.)
wis - dom, love most bright,
peace - ful mu - sic rings,
p

l, .s .f :m.r .d :s, .d .t,

mf Drawn by Thee, our souls, as - pir - ing,
p Where the flock, in Thee con - fid - ing,
mf(p)
Soar to un - cre -
Drink of joy from

r .m,f :m :r | d :— :
l₁ :t₁ .l₁ :t₁ | s₁
-a - ted light.
death - less springs.
f .r :s .m :f | m :— :
f₁ :s₁ :s₁ | d₁ :— :

f Word of God, our flesh that
cres. Theirs is beau - ty's fair - - est
f (cresc.)
A mi.

fash - ion'd,
plea - sure;
With the fire of life im -
f Theirs is wis - dom's ho - - liest
(*f*)

-pas - sion'd,
trea - sure;
dim.
Striv - - - ing
Thou dost
dim.

s :— :s | f :m :— | r :— :
d :— :d | d .t, :d :— | t, :— :
still to truth un - - known,
ev - - er lead Thine own,
s :m :m | f :s :l | r :— :
m :l :l, | r, :m, :f, | s, :— :
: : | m :— :f | s :— :m
p
d :— :d | d :s, :l,
Soar - ing, dy - ing
In the love of
s :— :l | s :m :m
d :t, :l, | m :m, :l,
p

r .m,f :r :— | d :— :— | : :
l, :t, .l, :t, | s, :— :— | : :
round Thy Throne.
joys un - - known.
f .r :s .m :f | m :— :— | : :
f, :s, :— | d, :— :— | : :
D.S.

41 JESU, LAMB OF GOD REDEEMER

Edited from *Gradualia* Lib.I. 1607
by R.R.TERRY

WILLIAM BYRD
(1543-1623)

(♩= about 72)

Key G mi.

SOPRANO — *p* — Je - su, Lamb of God, Re-deem - er

ALTO — *p* — Je - su, Lamb, Re - deem - er

TENOR (*8ve lower*) — *p* — Je - su, Lamb of God, Redeem - er

BASS — *p* — Je - su, Lamb of God, Re - deem - er

(♩= about 72)

For rehearsal only

cresc. *f* *dim.*

Born the Vir-gin Ma - - ry's Son Who, up-

Born the Vir-gin Ma - - ry's Son Who, up-

Born the Vir-gin Ma - - ry's Son Who, up-

Born the Vir - gin Ma - - ry's Son Who, up-

This anthem to be sung unaccompanied.

p
cresc.
-on the Cross a vic - tim, For man
-on the Cross a vic - tim, For
-on the Cross a vic-tim, For man hast
-on the Cross a vic - tim, For man
hast Sal - va - tion won, From whose side which
man Sal-va - tion won, From whose side which
Sal va - - tion won, From whose side which
hast Sal - va-tion won, From whose side which
dim.
mf

dolce
dim.
man had pierc - ed Flowed the wa - ter, and the blood
dolce
dim.
man had pierc - ed Flowed the wa - ter, and the blood
man had pierc - ed Flowed the wa-ter
man had pierc - ed Flowed the wa -
f
the blood, By Thy sa - cred bo - dy
f
and the blood, By Thy sa - cred bo - dy
f
and the blood, By Thy sa - cred bo - dy
f
-ter and the blood, By Thy sa - cred bo - dy
f

bro - ken In life and death be Thou our food. O gen - tle
bro - ken In life and death be Thou our food. O gen -
bro - ken In life and death be Thou our food. O gen -
bro - ken In life and death be Thou our food. O gen -
O ho - ly O ho - ly Je - su who di - edst
-tle O ho - ly O Je - su, Je - su who di -
-tle O ho - ly O Je - su who di -
-tle O ho - ly O Je - su who di - edst
p
mf
f
dim.

for us Lord, have mer-cy on
-edst for us Lord, have mer-cy on us, Lord, have mer-cy
-edst for us Lord, have mer-cy on us, Lord, have
for us Lord, have mer - cy on us
us Lord, have mercy on us, have mer - cy on
Lord, have mer-cy on us have mer - cy, mer - cy. on
mer - cy have mer - cy on us, have mer - cy on
Lord, have mer-cy on us, have mercy, have mer-cy on
dim.
pp

mf
f
us O gen - tle O ho - ly O ho - ly
us O gen - tle O ho - ly O ho -
us O gen - tle O ho - ly
us O gen - tle O ho - ly O ho - ly
dim.
p
Je - su, who di - edst for us Lord have
-ly, ho - ly Je - su; Lord, have mercy on us
O ho - ly Je - su, Je - su Lord, have mer-cy on us
Je - su who di - edst for us Lord, have mer-cy

mer - cy on us Lord, have mer - cy on
Lord, have mer - cy, Lord, have mer - cy on us, have mer - cy
Lord, have mer - cy on us, on us,
on us, Lord, have mer - cy on us have mer -
dim. p rall. pp
us, on us. A - - men.
on us. A - - - - men.
have mer - cy on us. A - - - - men.
-cy on us. A - - - men.
dim. p rall. pp

42 JESU, LAMB OF GOD, REDEEMER

WOLFGANG AMADEUS MOZART
(1756-91)

Cross a vic - tim hast man's sal - va - tion won,
Cross a vic - tim hast man's sal - va - tion won,
Cross a vic - tim hast man's sal - va - tion won,
Cross a vic - tim hast man's sal - va - tion won,
From Whose side, which man had
From Whose side, which man had
From Whose side, which man had
From Whose side, which man had

dim.
pierc - ed, Flow'd the wa - ter and the Blood,
dim.
pierc - ed, Flow'd the wa - ter and the Blood,
dim.
pierc - ed, Flow'd the wa - ter and the Blood,
dim.
pierc - ed, Flow'd the wa - ter and the Blood,
dim.
D3
pp
poco a poco cresc.
By Thy sa - cred Bo - dy bro - ken Be
pp
poco a poco cresc.
By Thy sa - cred Bo - dy bro - ken Be
pp
poco a poco cresc.
By Thy sa - cred Bo - dy bro - ken
pp
poco a poco cresc.
By Thy sa - cred Bo - dy bro - ken
poco a poco cresc.
pp

in life and death, our food, be Thou in life and
in life and death our food, be Thou in life,
Be in life our food, be Thou in life, in
Be in life our food, be Thou in life, in
mf
death, in life and death our food.
in life and death our food.
life and death our food.
life and death our food.
pp
rit.

43 JESU, LEAD MY FOOTSTEPS EVER

From 'CHRISTMAS ORATORIO'

English translation by
CHARLES SANFORD TERRY

JOHANN SEBASTIAN BACH
(1685-1750)
Edited by W. GILLIES WHITTAKER

NOTE: Expression marks in brackets refer to the repeat.
* When the Piano is used, octaves should be used by the left hand throughout.

foot - steps ev - er.
do - ings sev - er.
foot - steps ev - er.
do - ings sev - er.
cresc.
Ev - er
Put all
cresc.
Ev - er
Put all
cresc.
(cresc.)
dim.
(dim.)
p
cresc.
(pp)

all my sen - ses guide;
else than Thee a - side!
all my sen - ses guide;
else than Thee a - side!
mf
(cresc.)
dim.
mf
Je - su,
p
Je - su,
p
dim.
p

let Thy grace at - tend

cresc.

let Thy grace at - tend
let Thy grace at - tend

cresc.

let Thy grace at - tend

cresc.

me;

me;
me;

me;

mf dim.
From all e - vil e'er de -
mf dim.
From all e - vil e'er de -
mf dim.
- fend me.
p
p
- fend me.
p
L.H.
col 8
dim.
pp

44 JESU! THE VERY THOUGHT IS SWEET.

ST. BERNARD OF CLAIRVAUX (1091-1153)
Translated by J. M. NEALE

T. L. DA VITTORIA
(1540-1605)

The whole of this anthem should be sung *sotto voce*
This anthem to be sung unaccompanied.

heart - joys meet, all heart - - joys meet; But sweeter
- joys meet, all heart - joys meet; But sweet -
- joys meet, all heart - joys meet; But sweet -
- joys meet, all heart - joys meet; But sweeter than
dim.
than the hon - - - ey far,
er than the hon - - - ey far, sweet -
- er than the hon - - ey far, sweet -
the hon - ey far,
cresc.

sweet-er than the hon - ey far The glimp-ses
- er than the hon - ey far The glimp - ses
- er than the hon - ey far The glimp - ses
but sweet - er far The
of His Pres - ence are, of His Pres-ence are.
of His Pres - ence are, of His Pres-ence are.
of His Pres - ence are, of His Pres-ence are.
glimp - ses of His Pres - ence are.

45 JESU! THE VERY THOUGHT IS SWEET

ST. BERNARD OF CLAIRVAUX (1091–1153)
Translated by J. M. NEALE

Melody from 'PIAE CANTIONES' 1582
Arranged by CHARLES WOOD (1866–1926)

Adagio

Key G mi.

SOPRANO: Je - su! the ve - ry thought is sweet; In that dear Name

ALTO: Je - su! the ve-ry thought is sweet, is sweet, is sweet; In that dear

TENOR (8ve lower): Je - su! the ve-ry thought is sweet, is sweet, is sweet; In that dear

BASS: Je - su! the ve - ry thought is sweet, is sweet; In that dear

Adagio

(for rehearsal only)

This anthem to be sung unaccompanied and *sotto voce.*

Reprinted by permission of the Faith Press Ltd., 22, Buckingham St., Charing Cross, W.C.2

G mi.
all heart-joys meet. No word is
Name all heart - joys meet. No word is
Name all heart-joys meet. No word is
Name all heart-joys meet. No word is
sung more sweet than this, No sound is heard more
sung more sweet than this, No sound is heard more
sung more sweet than this, No sound is heard more
sung more sweet than this, No sound is heard more

full of bliss, Than Je - sus, Je - -
full of bliss, Than Je - sus, Je - -
full of bliss, Than Je - sus, Je -
full of bliss, Than Je - sus, Je - -
- - sus, Son of God most high.
- - sus, Son of God most high.
- - sus, Son of God most high.
- - sus, Son of God most high.

46 JESU, THE VERY THOUGHT OF THEE

ST. BERNARD OF CLAIRVAUX
(1091–1153)
Translated by E. CASWALL

EDWARD C. BAIRSTOW

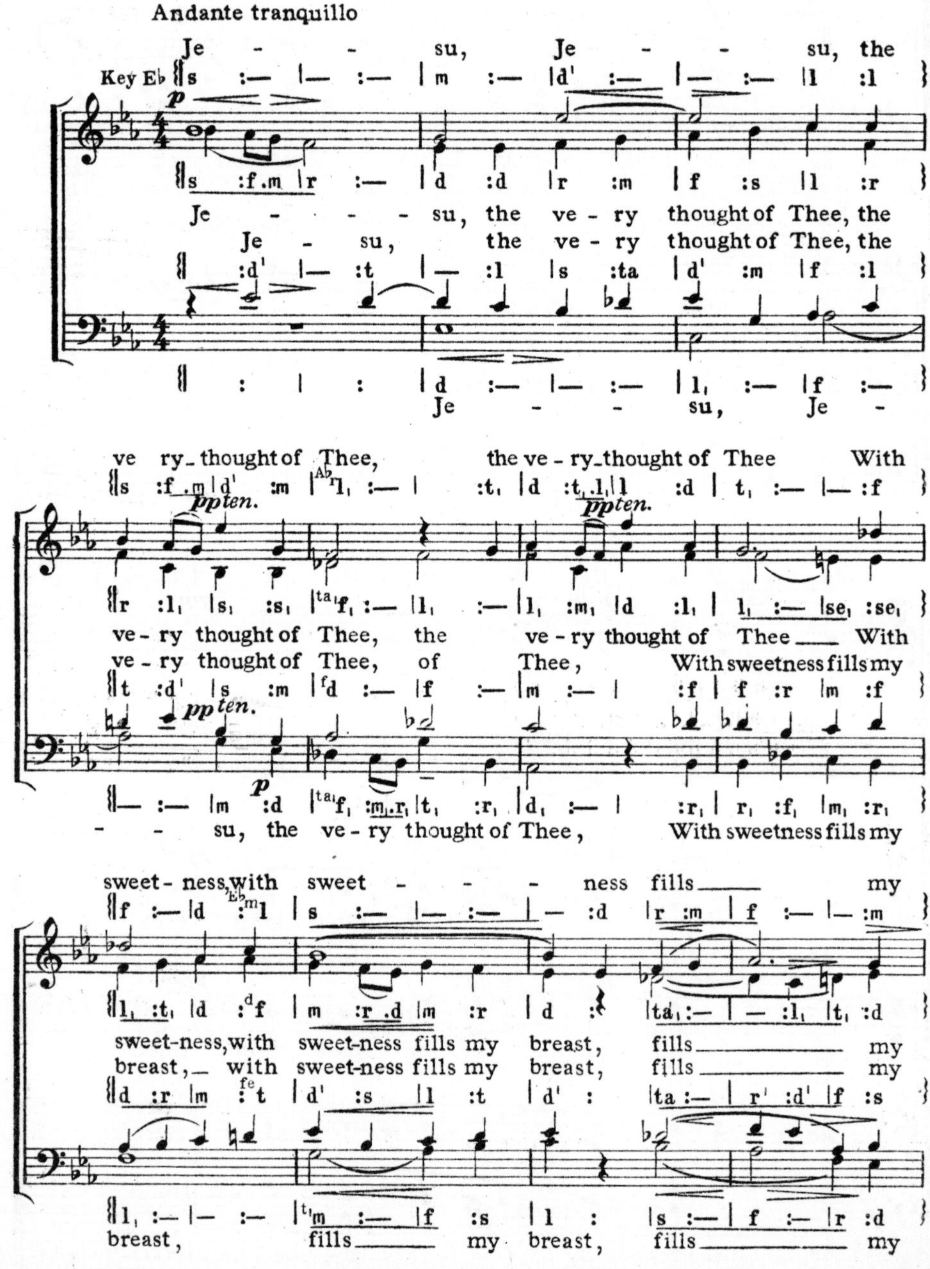

Andante tranquillo
Je - - su, Je - - su, the
Key E♭
Je - - - - su, the ve - ry thought of Thee, the
Je - su, the ve - ry thought of Thee, the
Je - - - su, Je -
ve ry thought of Thee, the ve - ry thought of Thee With
ve - ry thought of Thee, the ve - ry thought of Thee With
ve - ry thought of Thee, of Thee, With sweetness fills my
- - su, the ve - ry thought of Thee, With sweetness fills my
sweet - ness, with sweet - - - - ness fills my
sweet-ness, with sweet-ness fills my breast, fills my
breast, with sweet-ness fills my breast, fills my
breast, fills my breast, fills my

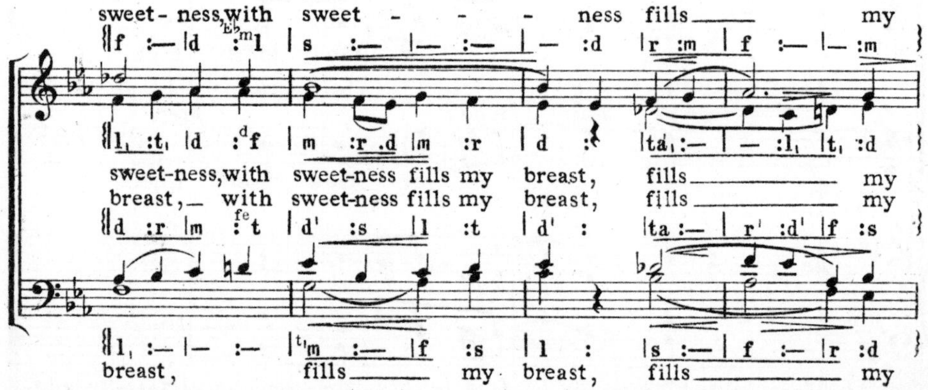

From 'Three Introits or Short Anthems', Oxford University Press.
This anthem may be sung unaccompanied.

breast; But sweeter far, but sweeter far, Thy
breast; But sweeter far, but sweet - er far, Thy
breast; But sweeter far, but sweet - - er sweet-er far, Thy
breast; But sweeter far, sweet - er far, Thy
face to see, Thy face to see, And
in Thy pres-ence rest, and
in Thy pres-ence rest, and in Thy pres-ence rest, and
in Thy pres-ence, in Thy pres-ence rest, Thy pres-ence rest, and
And in Thy pres-ence rest, and in Thy pres-ence rest, and
in Thy pres-sence rest, and in Thy pres - ence rest.

47

JUDGE ME, O GOD

Psalm xliii

FELIX MENDELSSOHN-BARTHOLDY (1809–47)

Con moto
Key D mi.
TENOR
BASS
Judge me, O God, and plead, and plead my cause a-gainst an un-
(for rehearsal only)
SOPRANO
O de-liv-er me from de-ceit-ful and un-just men.
CONTRALTO
-god-ly na - - - - - - - tion; For
Thou art the God, Thou art the God of my strength; O why dost Thou

This anthem may be sung unaccompanied.

SOPRANO
Where-fore mourn I be-cause the en - e - my
CONTRALTO
cast me from Thee?
sore-ly op-press-eth me?
Send out Thy light,
TEN.
Send out Thy light, Thy light and
BASS

Thy light and truth, Lord; O let them lead me and bring me
truth, Lord; O let them lead me, and bring me
lead me and bring me
un - to Thy ho - ly hill, and to Thy dwelling place, and
un - to Thy ho - ly hill, and to Thy dwelling place, and

Andante
to Thy dwell - ing place.
mf
to Thy dwell - ing place. And then will I go to the al - tar of
Andante
mf
And then will I go to the
TEN.
BASS
God, the God of my joy,

al - tar of God, the God of my joy.
to God, the
cresc.
to God, the God of my
sf
God of my glad-ness and joy.
cresc.

glad-ness and joy.
I will praise Thee up - on the harp, O my
I will praise Thee up - on the harp, O my God,
TEN.
God, I will
BASS
God,

praise Thee, O my God, will praise Thee up - on the
praise Thee, will praise Thee, O God, will praise Thee up - on the
praise Thee, O my God, will praise Thee up - on the
harp, O my God, will praise Thee up - on the harp, O my
harp, O my God, will praise Thee up - on the harp, O my
dim.
rit.

Allegro moderato
God. O my soul, why art thou cast down - ward, and why art
God, my God, my
God, my God,
Allegro moderato *
thou dis-qui-et-ed with-in me? Hope in the Lord,
God, my my God. Hope in the Lord,
my God. Hope in the Lord,

* If desired, organ may well be allowed to enter here.

hope in the Lord.
hope in the Lord, O my soul, for I will praise Him,
Hope in the Lord, hope in the Lord, O my
Hope in the Lord, hope in the Lord, O my

soul, for I will praise Him who is the health of my
soul, for I will praise Him who is the health of my
coun-te-nance, and my gra-cious Lord and God.
coun-te-nance, and my gra-cious Lord and God.

48 KING OF GLORY, KING OF PEACE

GEORGE HERBERT
(1593-1632)

Choral (Jesu, meines Herzens Freud) *J. R. AHLE* (1660)
Harmonised by JOHANN SEBASTIAN BACH
(1685-1750)
Arr. by W. H. HARRIS

*May be sung Full throughout

SOLI
(or Semi-Chorus)
nev - er cease, I will move Thee. Thou hast grant-ed
Ped
CHORUS
mf cresc.
my re-quest, Thou hast heard me; Thou didst note my
dim.
work-ing breast, Thou hast spared me. Thou, thou hast
p

spared me.
Where-fore with my
p sostenuto
Manual
ut - most art I will sing Thee,
And the cream of all my heart I will bring Thee.
Ped.

Though my sins a - gainst me cried, Thou didst clear
Man.
me; And a - lone, when they re-plied, Thou didst hear
dim.
Thou didst hear
me.
Thou, thou didst hear me.
SOLO
rit.
Ped.

f a tempo
Seven whole days, not one in seven, I will praise
f a tempo
f a tempo
E mi
Thee; In my heart, though not in heaven, I can raise
A mi.
Thee. Small it is in this poor sort

To en - rol Thee:
E'en e - ter - ni - ty's too short
to ex - tol Thee.
To ex - tol Thee,
rall.
a tempo
Ped.

49 LEAD ME, LORD

from 'PRAISE THE LORD, O MY SOUL'

The four bars of introduction are optional.

mf
make Thy way plain be - fore my face.
(SOPRANO)
For it is Thou, Lord, Thou, Lord, on - ly, that
cresc.
dim.
mak- - est me dwell in ___ safe - ty.
cresc.
p

CHORUS

‖s :— |f :m |l :— |s :— |s :m |d :f |m :— |r :r }

cresc.

‖d :— |t, :d |d :— |d :— |d :— |d :— |d :— |t, :r }

For it is Thou, Lord, Thou, — Lord, — on - ly, that

‖s :— |s :s |l :— |d' :— |d :— |f :— |s :— |s :t }

cresc.

‖m :— |r :d |f :— |m :— |m, :— |l, :— |s, :— |s :f }

pp

cresc.

‖s :— |l :t |d' :— |r :m .f |m :— |r :— |d :— |— :— ‖

dim. *p* *rit.*

‖m :— |m :m |m :— |d :— |d :— |t, :— |d :— |— :— ‖

mak - est me dwell in — safe - - ty.

‖t :— |l :se |l :— |l :— |s :— |— :f |m :— |— :— ‖

dim. *p* *rit.*

‖m :r |d :t, |l, :s, |f, :— |s, :— |— :— |d :— |— :— ‖

dim. *rit.*

50 LET THY MERCIFUL EARS O LORD

Reprinted by permission from the Tudor Church Music Series (Oxford University Press)
This anthem to be sung unaccompanied.

-tain, may ob - tain their pe - ti - tions,
that they may ob - tain their pe - ti - tions, make
-tain their pe - ti - tions, make them to
ob - tain their pe - ti - tions,
make them to ask such things,
them to ask, to ask such things, make
ask such things, such things, make them to
make them to ask such things make them to ask such
make them to ask such things as shall please
dim. e poco rit.
them to ask such things as shall please, shall please
ask such things as shall please Thee, shall please
things as shall please Thee, shall please
A - men.
p slightly slower
Thee; through Je - sus Christ our Lord, our Lord. A - men.

51 LET US NOW PRAISE FAMOUS MEN

From Ecclesiasticus xliv

know - ledge: Such as found out mu-si-cal tunes,
p subito
and re - ci - ted ver-ses in wri - ting: All these were
honoured in their gen-er-a-tions, and were the glo - ry of their
largamente
times. And some there be which have
pp subito

no me - mo - ri - al; who are perished as though they had nev - er
been. Their bo - dies are bu - ried in
peace; but their name liv-eth for ev - er -
- more.
pp
cresc.
f
ff
8ve

52 LO, ROUND THE THRONE A GLORIOUS BAND

From 'Six Short Anthems for the Seasons of the Church', Oxford University Press.

NOTE: This anthem is also published in an extended version for chorus, semi-chorus, and orchestra or organ: full score and parts on hire.

f :s :m | r :— : | d' :-.ta:l | s :f :m | r :r :r | l :— :t | d' :-.t :l
SOPRANOS
-le - lu - jah! Through tri - bu - la - tion great they
f :s :m | r :— :
rit.
a tempo
pp
p
Sw.
senza Ped.
s :— :l | t :— :d' | r' :— :l | d' :l :t | l :— :l | d' :— :l | s :— :r
mp
came: they bore the Cross, de - spised the shame: from all their la - bours
pp
f :-.m :r | d :— :d | f :— :s | l :— :s | f :d' :— | l :— :s | f :s :m
now_they rest, in God's e - ter - nal glo-ry blest. Hal-le - lu-

f DESCANT
jah! They see their Sa-viour face—to
f T. & B. in unison
Gt.
cresc.
Gt.
f Full Sw.
Ped.
face, and sing—the Tri-umphs of—His grace: Him day—and
night they cease-less praise, to Him the loud—thanks-giv-ing

* The small notes are optional.

raise: Hal - le - lu - jah!
ff
Gt.
ff
Wor - thy the Lamb, for sin - ners slain, through
ff
Wor - thy the Lamb, for sin - ners slain, through
ff
Wor - thy the Lamb, for sin - ners slain, through
ff
Wor - thy the Lamb, for sin - ners slain, through

end - less years to live and reign: Thou hast re -
end - less years to live and reign: Thou hast re -
end - less years to live and reign: Thou hast re -
end - less years to live and reign: Thou hast re -
-deemed us by Thy Blood, and made us
-deemed us by Thy Blood, and made us
-deemed us by Thy Blood, and made us
-deemed us by Thy Blood, and made us

cresc.
kings and priests to God. Hal - le - lu -
cresc.
kings and priests to God. Hal - le - lu -
cresc.
kings and priests to God. Hal - le - lu -
cresc.
kings and priests to God. Hal - le - lu -
jah!
jah!
jah!
jah!
ff
Gt.

D is Ray
mf a little slower
O may we tread the sa - cred road that Saints and ho - ly Mar-tyrs
mf
p
p Ch. a little slower
senza Ped.
f F
f
cres -
trod: Wage to the end the glo - rious strife, and win like them a
f Sw.
Ch & Sw.
cresc.
-cen - do ff
fff
molto rit.
crown of life. Hal - le - lu - jah A - men.
Gt.
ff
Gt.
cresc.
Ped.

53 LO! STAR-LED CHIEFS

From the oratorio *Palestine*
Words by REGINALD HEBER (1783-1826)

Wm. CROTCH
(1775-1847)

N.B. The Bass notes between the brackets thus ⌊ ⌋ also all lower octave passages may be played on the pedals when the accompaniment is played on the Organ.

Key G
SOPRANO
ALTO
TENOR
BASS
dim.
Lo! star-led chiefs As -
Lo! star-led chiefs, lo!
- sy-rian o-dours bring, And bend - ing Ma - gi
star-led chiefs As - sy - rian o - dours bring, And bend-ing Ma - gi,
seek their in-fant King,
bend - ing Ma - gi, and bend - ing Ma - gi
bend - ing Ma - gi, bend - ing Ma - gi

Lo! star-led
seek their in-fant King! Lo! star-led chiefs As-
Lo! star-led
chiefs As-sy-rian o-dours bring, And bend-ing Ma-gi,
-sy-rian o-dours bring, And bend-ing Ma-gi,
chiefs As-sy-rian o-dours bring,
bend-ing Ma-gi seek their
bend-ing Ma-gi, and bend-ing Ma-gi seek their

in - fant King! bend - ing Ma-gi seek their in - fant King!
bend - ing Ma - gi, bend - ing Ma-gi seek their in - fant King!
in - fant King! seek their in - fant King!
in - fant King! bend - ing Ma-gi seek their in - fant King!
Mark'd ye,
mark'd ye, where, hov'r-ing o'er His head,
mark'd ye, where, hov'r-ing hov'r-ing o'er His
mark'd ye, where, hov'r-ing o'er His head,

hov'r-ing o'er His head, o'er His ra-diant head, The
head, hov'r-ing o'er His head, o'er His ra-diant
hov'r-ing o'er His head, hov'r-ing o'er His ra - diant
dove's white wings ce - les - tial, ce-les - tial
cresc.
head, The dove's white wings ce - les - tial
cresc.
cresc.
f
dim.
glo - ry shed, ce - les - tial
f
dim.
f
dim.

glo - ry shed, ce - les - tial glo - ry shed?
Lo! star-led chiefs As - sy - rian o - dours bring,
As - sy - rian o - dours bring, As - sy - rian o - dours
As - sy - rian o - dours bring,
Lo! star-led chiefs As - sy - rian o - dours bring,

And bend-ing Ma - - gi
bring, And bend-ing Ma - - gi seek their
And bend-ing Ma - gi seek their in-fant, in - fant
And bend-ing Ma - gi,
seek their in-fant King! Mark'd ye,
in - fant King!
King, seek their in-fant King! Mark'd ye,
and bend-ing Ma - gi! Mark'd ye,

mark'd — ye, where, hov'r-ing o'er His head, where
mark'd — ye, where, hov'r-ing o'er His ra-diant
mark'd ye, where, hov'r-ing o'er His head,
hovr-ing o'er His head, o'er His ra-diant head, The
head, o'er His ra-diant head, o'er His ra-diant
o'er His ra-diant head, o'er His ra-diant head,
dove's white wings ce - les - tial, ce-les - tial
cresc.
head, The dove's white wings ce - les - tial
cresc.
cresc.

glo - ry shed? o'er His
simile
ra - diant head, Mark'd ye, where, hov'r - ing
The dove's white_ wings ce - les - tial
o'er His ra-diant head, The dove's white wings ce - les - tial
Mark'd ye, where, hov'r - ing, The dove's white_ wings ce - les - tial

glo - ry shed, The dove's white wings ce - les - tial
glo - - ry shed, The dove's white wings ce - les - tial
glo - ry shed, The dove's white wings ce - les - tial
glo - ry shed?
rall.
dim
p
pp

54 LORD, FOR THY TENDER MERCIES' SAKE

Words from Lidley's Prayers (c.1566) *Attributed to the school of Dr. TYE* (1505–72)

Lento ma non troppo

Key F

SOP. *p*

ALTO

Lord, for Thy ten-der mer-cies' sake, lay not our

TEN. *p*

BASS

to our charge,

sins to our charge, but for-give that is past, and give us grace to a-

-mend our sin-ful lives, to de-cline from sin and in-cline to vir-

tue, ——— that we may walk with a

mp

tue, that we may walk with a per-fect

tue, that we may walk with a per-fect heart, a per-fect

mp

-tue that we may walk with a per-fect heart, with a per-fect

This anthem should be sung unaccompanied and may well be transposed a tone higher.

per - fect heart, that we may walk with a per - fect
cresc.
heart, that we may walk with a per - fect
heart, that we may walk with a per - fect heart, with a per - fect
cresc.
heart be - fore Thee now and ev - er - more,
dim.
mf
heart be - fore Thee now and ev - er - more, that
heart be - fore Thee now and ev - er - more, that we may walk with a
dim.
mf
that we may walk with a per - fect heart, that we may
we may walk with a per - fect heart, that we may
per - fect heart, a per - fect heart, that we may walk with a per - fect
per - fect heart, with a per - fect heart, that we may walk with a per - fect
dim. e rall.
pp
walk with a per - fect heart be - fore Thee now and ev - er - more.
heart, with a per - fect heart be - fore Thee now and ev - er - more.

55 LORD, IT BELONGS NOT TO MY CARE

RICHARD BAXTER
(1615–91)

H. WALFORD DAVIES

May best be sung unaccompanied. [Ed.]

cresc.
give. If life be long, I will be _ glad That I may long o -
cresc.
give. If _ life ______ be _ long, Then I may long o -
cresc.
bey: If _ short-yet why should I be sad; To soar to end-less day.
why sad? ______
p SOLO
Christ leads us through no _ dark - er rooms Than He went thro' be -

Must en-ter by this
SOLO
He that comes.— Must en-ter by— this
He that un-to God's kingdom comes Must en-ter by— this
SOLO
pp
p cresc.
fore
p cresc.
when grace has made me meet Thy
G# mi.
CHORUS
1st Choir
door. Come Lord, when grace has made me
when grace has made me meet Thy
CHORUS
2nd Choir
Come Lord, when grace has made me meet, Thy

bles - sed face to see;
F♯ mi.
meet Thy face to see;
1st Choir
bles - sed face to see;
For if Thy work on earth be sweet
bles - sed face to see; For, if Thy work be sweet,
2nd Choir
bles - sed face to see; If work be sweet,

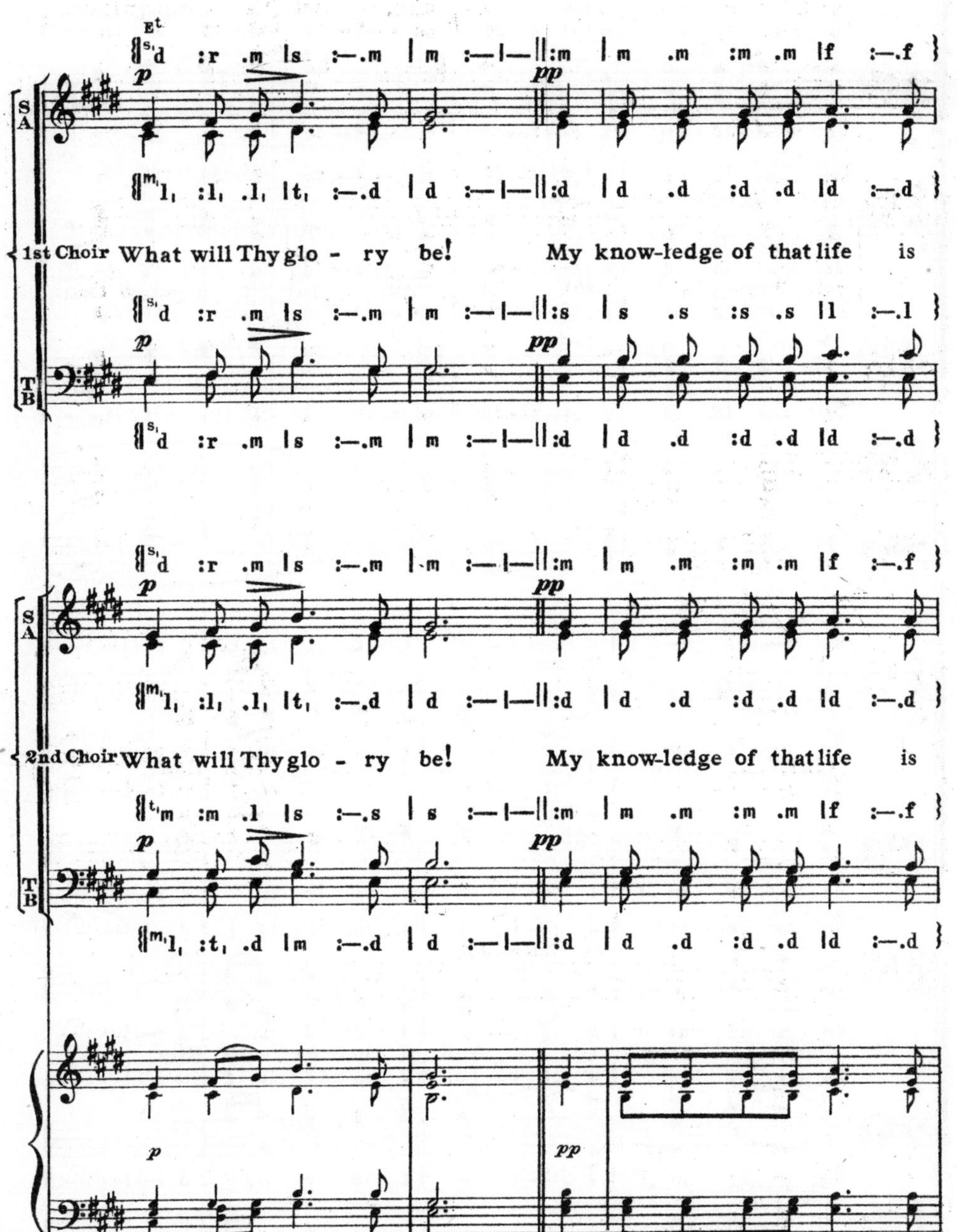
1st Choir What will Thy glo - ry be! My know-ledge of that life is
2nd Choir What will Thy glo - ry be! My know-ledge of that life is

cresc.
small, The eye of faith is dim; But 'tis e-nough that
cresc.
cresc.
small, The eye of faith is dim; But 'tis e-nough that
cresc.
cresc.
pp
Christ knows all, And I shall be with Him.
pp
pp
Christ knows all, And I shall be with Him.
pp
pp

56 LORD, I FLEE TO THEE FOR REFUGE

LASS, O HERR, MICH HÜLLE FINDEN

FELIX MENDELSSOHN-BARTHOLDY
(1809-47)

Andante
Key E♭
SOLO CONTRALTO
Lord, I flee to Thee for re-fuge, Bow Thine ear un-
-to my pray'r; If my sins Thou shouldst re-mem-ber, Ev - er-more must
I des-pair, Ev - er-more must I des-pair.

CHORUS
p SOPRANO
Lord, I flee to Thee for re-fuge, Bow Thine ear un-
p ALTO
Lord, I flee to Thee for re-fuge, Bow Thine ear un-
p TENOR
Lord, I flee to Thee for re-fuge, Bow Thine ear un-
p BASS
Lord, O Lord, Bow Thine ear un-
p
-to my pray'r. If my sins Thou shouldst re-mem-ber,
cresc.
-to my pray'r. If my sins Thou shouldst re-mem-ber,
-to my pray'r. If my sins Thou shouldst re-mem-ber,
-to my pray'r. If my sins Thou shouldst re-mem-ber,
cresc.

Ev-er-more, ev-er-more, ev-er-more must I des-pair.
Ev-er-more, ev-er-more, ev-er-more must I des-pair.
Ev-er-more, ev-er-more, ev-er-more must I des-pair.
Ev-er-more, ev-er-more, ev-er-more must I des-pair.
cresc.
SOLO
Shall my trou-bles last for ev-er? Is grief my dai-ly lot?
Weak and help-less must I lan-guish, By my God, a-las, for-

TUTTI
Shall my trou - bles
TUTTI cresc.
-got? Shall my trou - bles last for ev - er, for
TUTTI cresc.
Shall my trou - bles last for ev - er, for ev - er,
TUTTI cresc.
Shall my trou - bles last for-
p
cresc.
mf
last for ev - er, Shall my trou - bles last for
ev - er, Shall my trou - bles last for ev - -
Shall my trou - bles, Shall my trou - bles last for ev - er,
ev - er, for ev - er, Shall my trou - bles last for
f

C mi.
D 5
G mi.
ev - - er, And is grief my dai-ly lot? Weak and
- er, And is grief my dai-ly lot? Weak and
And is grief my dai-ly lot?
ev - - er, And is grief my dai-ly lot? Weak and
help - less must I lan - guish, By my God, a - las, for -
help - less must I lan - guish, By my God, a - las, for -
Weak and help - less must I lan - guish, By my God for -
help - less must I lan - guish, By my God, a - las, for -

pp
-got? O Lord, O Lord,
SOLO
-got? O Lord, O Lord, I flee to
-got? O Lord, O Lord,
-got? O Lord, O Lord,
pp
p TUTTI cresc.
If my sins Thou
Thee for re-fuge, Bow Thine ear un - to my prayer. If my sins Thou
If my sins Thou
If my sins Thou
p cresc.

Gmi.t
shouldst re-mem-ber, Ev - er-more must
shouldst re-mem - ber, Ev - er-more must
shouldst re-mem-ber, Ev - er-more must
shouldst re-mem - ber, Ev - er-more must
I des-pair,
fE♭
SOLO
I des-pair, Ev - er-more must I des-pair.
I des-pair,
I des-pair,
pp

NOTE: **Whenever possible this anthem should be immediately followed by the next.**

56a LORD, MY TRUST IS IN THY MERCY

FELIX MENDELSSOHN-BARTHOLDY
(1809-47)

*If this is sung as a separate anthem the word 'Lord' may be used.

CHORUS
SOPRANO
ALTO
Lord, my trust is in Thy mer - cy, All my hope in
TENOR
BASS
Lord, my trust is in Thy mer - cy, All my hope in
sempre legato
Lord, my trust is in Thy mer - cy,
Thee I place, All my hope, all
Lord, my trust is in Thy mer - cy,
Thee I place, My trust is in Thy mer - cy,

{|s :— .s |f :— .f |m :l |r :— |s :— .d |d :t₁ }

All my hope in Thee I place, I will sing Thy

{|— :m₁ .m |m :r |r :d |t :— |s₁ :— .s₁ |l₁ :s₁ }

my hope in Thee I place, I will sing Thy

{|s :— .s |f :— .f |m :l |r :— |d :— .d |f :r }

All my hope in Thee I place, I will sing Thy

{|t₁ :d |l₁ :t₁ |d :fe₁ |s₁ :— .f₁ |m₁ :— .m₁ |r₁ :f₁ }

All my hope in Thee I place, I will sing Thy

{|s :— .d |d :t₁ |d .r :m .s |f .m :r .d |d :t₁ |d :— }

lov - ing kind-ness, And the won-der of Thy grace,

{|s₁ :— .s₁ |l₁ :s₁ |s₁ :— .m₁ |f₁ .s₁ :l₁ .d |r₁ :m₁ |m₁ :— }

lov - ing kind-ness, And the won-der of Thy grace,

{|d :— .s |f :r |s .f :m .r |d :f .m |r :r |d :— }

lov - ing kind-ness, And the won-der of Thy grace,

{|m₁ :— .m |r :f |m .r :d .ta₁ |l₁ .s₁ :f₁ |s₁ :se₁ |l₁ :— }

lov - ing kind-ness, And the won-der of Thy grace,

and the wonder,
and the wonder, der, the
and the won - der of Thy grace,
and the won - der,
and the won - der of Thy grace.
won - - - der of Thy grace.
and the won - der of Thy grace.
and the won - der of Thy grace.

SOLO
Lord, my trust is in Thy mer - cy, All my hope in
Thee I place, I will sing Thy lov - ing kind - ness,
And the won - der of Thy grace. I will sing Thy
lov - ing kind - ness, And the won - der of Thy grace,

E♭ maj.
BASS f TUTTI
And the won-der of Thy grace. Lord, my trust is
B♭t
TENOR f TUTTI
Lord, my trust is
in Thy mer-cy, All my
f E♭
in Thy mer-cy, All my hope in
hope in Thee I place,

TUTTI
Lord, my trust is
TUTTI
Lord, my trust is in Thy mer-cy. All my
Thee, all my hope in Thee I place. Lord, my
All my hope in Thee I place, Lord, my
in Thy mer-cy, All my hope
hope in Thee I place,
trust is in Thy mer-cy, All my hope
trust is in Thy mer-cy, All my hope in

in Thee I place, in Thee,
Lord, my trust is in Thy mer - cy, in Thy mer - cy,
in Thee I place, All my hope, my
Thee I place, Lord, my hope is
Lord, my trust is in Thy mer - cy,
Lord, my trust is in Thy mer - cy, All my hope in
hope in Thee I place, Lord, my trust is
in Thy mer - cy, All my hope in Thee I place,

All my hope in Thee I place, Lord,
Thee I place, Lord my trust is
in Thy mer - - cy,
in Thee I place,
(sempre legato)
Lord, my trust is in Thy mer - cy,
in Thy mer - cy, All my hope in Thee I
Lord, my trust is in Thy mer - cy, Lord, my trust is
Lord, Lord,
più f

f Eb
s r' :— |d' :— |f' :— |— :— |— :r' |t :d'

All my hope ___ in Thee I

ta f :— |m :d' |t :l |s :— .l |t :r |f :f

place, ___ All my hope in Thee I

f d' .t :l .s |m' :— .m' |r' :d' |t :— .d' |r' :r' |r' :d'

in_ Thy mer - cy, All ___ my hope in Thee I

— :— |— :— |— :— (d)s :— .s |s :s |t :l

___ All my hope in Thee I

L.H. ff

r' :— |— : | : | : | : | :

place;

f :— |— : |d' :— .m |m :r |d' :— .m |m :f

f SOLO

place; I will sing Thy lov - ing kind-ness,

t :— |— : | : | : | : | :

place;

s :— |— : | : | : | : | :

place;

p

f TUTTI
I will sing Thy
And the won-der of Thy grace.
I will sing Thy
f TUTTI
I will sing Thy
f TUTTI
I will sing Thy
lov - ingkind-ness, And the won-der of Thy grace,
lov - ingkind-ness, And the won-der of Thy grace,
lov - ingkind-ness, And the won-der of Thy grace,
lov - ingkind-ness, And the won-der of Thy grace,

and the wonder
and the wonder of Thy grace, the wonder
and the won - - der,
and the won-der, the won-der of Thy grace,
of Thy grace, and the won - der
of Thy grace, and the won - der
and the won-der, and the won -
and the won - - der of Thy

of Thy grace, Lord, the
of Thy grace, Lord, the won-der, Lord, the
SOLO
TUTTI
der of Thy grace, Lord, the
grace, Thy grace, Lord, the
won-der of Thy grace,
won-der of Thy grace, of Thy grace, I will
SOLO
TUTTI
SOLO
won-der of Thy grace,
won-der of Thy grace,

r :d |f :m |l :s |f :m |d' :— |s :—
sing Thy lov - ing kind - ness, lov - ing kind - ness,
m' :— |t, :— |d' :— |t :l |s :— |f :r |d :— |— :—
And the won - der of Thy grace.
s :— |f :— |m :— |re :— |m :— |t, :— |d :— |— :—
TUTTI
And the won - der of Thy grace.
m' :— |r' :— |d' :— |d' :— |d' :— |r :f |m :— |— :—
And the won - der of Thy grace.
d' :— |se :— |l :— |fe :— |s :— |s, :— |d :— |— :—
And the won - der of Thy grace.

57 MAN THAT IS BORN OF A WOMAN

FROM THE BURIAL SERVICE

Job xiv, 1.2.3.

SAMUEL SEBASTIAN WESLEY
(1810–76)

NOTE: This anthem was composed to precede 'Thou knowest, Lord' by Purcell, No. 88

cresc.
dim.
p
mis-e-ry. He cometh up, and is cut down, like a flow-er; he
G mi.
D mi.
fle-eth as it were a sha-dow, and nev-er con-
mf
dim.
-tin-u-eth, nev-er con-tin-u-eth in one stay.
in one, in one stay.

In the midst of life we are in death: of whom may we
f G mi.
Thee, O Lord,
seek for suc - cour, but of Thee, of Thee, O Lord,
suc - cour but of Thee, O Lord,
f C mi.
G mi.
Who for our sins art just - ly dis - pleas - ed? Yet, O Lord

cresc.
God most ho - ly, O Lord most might-y O
cresc.
f
cresc.
f
D4
4 G mi.
cresc.
ff
p
ho - ly and most mer-ci-ful Sa - viour, de - liv-er us not in - to the
de - liv - er us not
cresc.
ff
p
p
de-liv-er us not
cresc.
ff
p
Ped.
p rall.
pp
bit - ter, the bit - ter pains of e - ter - nal death.
in - to the bit - ter pains of e - ter - nal death.
p rall.
pp
p rall.
pp

58 MOST GLORIOUS LORD OF LYFE

EDMUND SPENSER (1552-1599) — CECIL ARMSTRONG GIBBS

Lento, molto maestoso — *poco più mosso*

Key B♭

SOP. ALTO TEN. BASS

Most glo-rious Lord ___ of Lyfe! that, on this day, Didst make Thy tri - - umph ov-er death and sin;

And hav - ing har - - row'd hell, ___ didst

And hav - ing har - row'd hell, didst

bring a - way Cap - tiv - it - y thence cap - tive, us ___

From the Oxford Series of Modern Anthems by permission.
This anthem may be sung unaccompanied.

* These two bars may be sung by Contraltos alone.

sin, May live for ev - er in fel -
sin, May live for ev - er in fel -
sin, May live for ev - er in fel -
sin, May live for ev - er in fel -
- ic - it - y! And that Thy love
- ic - it - y! And that Thy love
we weigh - ing worth - i - ly, May like - wise
we weigh - ing worth - i - ly, May like - - - wise
May like - wise
love Thee for the same, a - gaine; And for Thy

sake that all lyke deare didst buy, With
And for Thy sake, that all lyke deare didst buy, With
love may one an - o - ther en - - ter - tayne!
So let us love, deare Love, lyke as we ought,
Love is the les - son Which the Lord us taught.
senza rit.
senza rit.

59 MY SOUL, THERE IS A COUNTRY

poco rit.
sen-try, A sen-try, All skil-ful in the wars:
sen-try, All skil - - ful in the wars:
sen-try, All skil-ful, all skil-ful in the wars:
sen-try, All skil - - ful in the wars:
Daintily
There, a-bove noise and dan - ger, Sweet
There, a-bove noise and dan - ger, Sweet
There, a-bove noise and dan - ger, Sweet
There, a-bove noise and dan - ger, Sweet
Daintily

Peace sits crowned with smiles And One, born in a
Peace sits crowned with smiles And One, born in a
Peace sits crowned with smiles And One, born in a
Peace sits crowned with smiles And One, born in a
man - ger Com-mands the beau - teous files. He is thy
man - ger Com-mands the beau - teous files. He is thy
man - ger Com-mands the beau - teous files. He is thy
man - ger Com-mands the beau - teous files. He is thy
Slower
Slower

Animato

gra - - cious friend, And — O my soul a-

gra - cious friend, And — O my soul a-

gra - - cious friend, And — O my soul a-

gra - - cious friend, And — O my soul a-

Animato

Slower

pp espress.

-wake! Did — in pure love des - cend —

-wake! Did — in pure love des - - cend —

-wake! Did — in pure love des -

-wake! Did — in pure love des -

Slower

pp espress.

dim.
To die here for thy sake.
pp
dim.
To die here for thy sake.
pp
dim.
-cend To die here for thy sake.
pp
dim.
-cend To die here for thy sake.
pp
dim.
Tempo
p dolce
If thou canst get but thi - - - ther, There
p dolce
If thou canst get but thi - - - ther,
p dolce
If thou canst get but thi - - ther,
p dolce
If thou canst get but thi - - - ther,
Tempo
p dolce

cresc.
grows the flow'r of Peace, The Rose that can-not
There grows the flow'r of Peace, The Rose that can-not
There grows the flow'r of Peace, The Rose that can-not
There grows the flow'r of Peace, The Rose that can-not
wi-ther, Thy for-tress, and thy ease.
wi-ther, Thy for-tress, and thy ease.
wi-ther, Thy for-tress, and thy ease.
wi-ther, Thy for-tress, and thy ease.

Animato
Leave then thy fool - ish rang - es, For
Leave then thy fool - ish rang - es, For
Leave then thy fool - ish rang - es, For
Leave then thy fool - ish rang - es, For
Animato
none can thee se - cure But One who nev - er
none can thee se - cure But One,
none can thee se - cure But One,
none can thee se - cure But One who nev - er

cresc.
chang - es, One who nev - er chang - es, Thy
mf
One who nev - er chang - es, One who nev - er
mf
One who nev - er chang - es, One who nev - er
cresc.
chang - es, But One who nev - er chang - es, who
cresc.
God, thy life, thy cure,
chang - es, Thy God, thy life, thy
chang - es, who nev - er chang - - - - - -
nev - er chang - - - - - - - -

* From this point the nine bars in brackets may be sung by 2nd Sopranos if desirable.

chang - - - - - - - - - - - - - - -
One who nev-er chang - - - - - - - - -
chang - - - - - es, who nev-er chang - - -
— One who nev-er chang - es, One who
Allargando
Poco rit.
- - - - - - es, None can thee se - cure But
- - - - - - es, None can thee se - cure But
- - - - - - es, None can thee se - cure But
nev - er chang - es, None can thee se - cure But
Allargando
Poco rit.

Slower
One who nev-er chang-es, Thy God,
Slower
Thy life, Thy cure.
Slower

60 NOW THAT THE SUN HATH VEIL'D HIS LIGHT

(ON A GROUND)

WILLIAM FULLER
(1608-75)

HENRY PURCELL
(1658-95)
Arranged by
W. GILLIES WHITTAKER

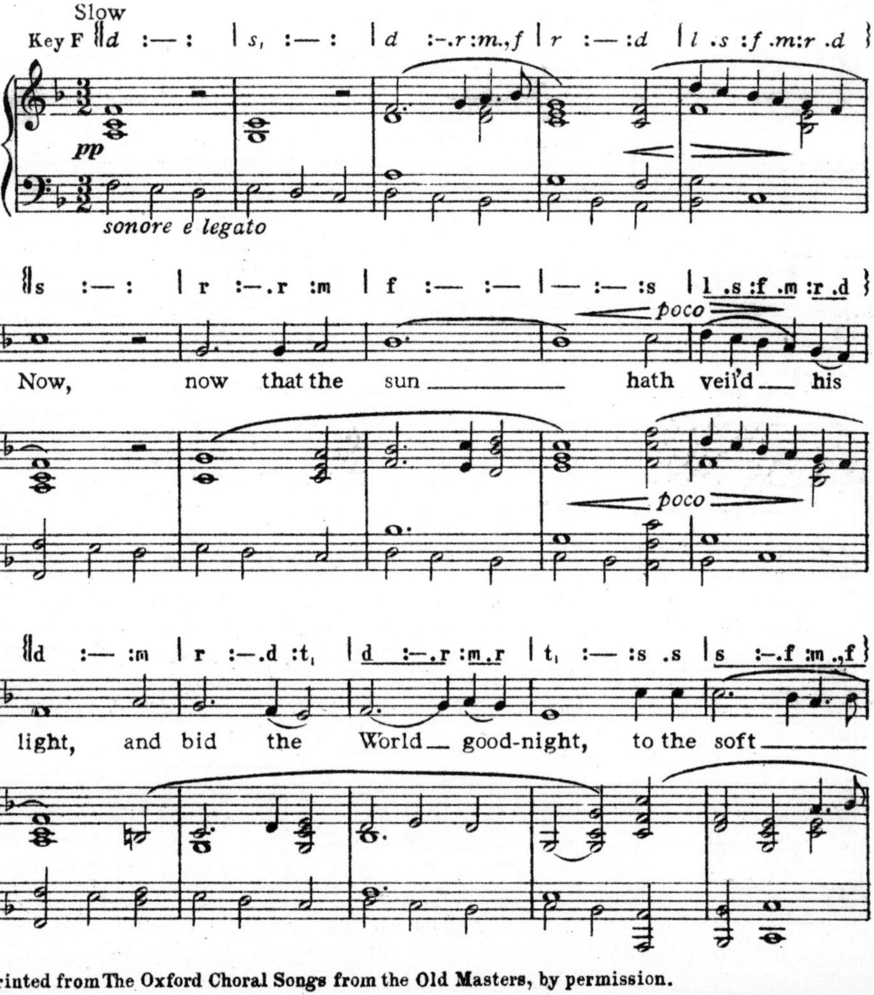

Slow

Key F ‖d :— : | s, :— : | d :-.r :m.,f | r :— :d | l .s :f .m:r .d

pp

sonore e legato

‖s :— : | r :-.r :m | f :— :— | — :— :s | l .s :f .m :r .d

poco

Now, now that the sun ______ hath veil'd ___ his

poco

‖d :— :m | r :-.d :t, | d :-.r :m.r | t, :— :s .s | s :-.f :m .,f

light, and bid the World ___ good-night, to the soft ______

Bed, to the soft, the soft_ Bed_ my Body I_ dis-
cresc.
mp
-pose, but where, where shall my soul re-pose? Dear,
cresc.
mp
poco
_ dear _ God, _ ev-en in Thy Arms, ev'n _
poco
p
poco
_ in_ Thy Arms, and can there be a - ny so
p
poco

A mi.t
sweet se - cu - ri - ty! Can there
be, a - ny so sweet, so sweet se -
poco
poco
- cu - ri - ty! Then to thy rest,
pp
pp
O my Soul!

(cresc.)

‖d' :— :d' .d' | d' :— :— | — :d',r'.m' :r' .d' | d' :— :d's ,,f }

Then to thy rest, O my Soul! and sing

‖m ,,f :r ,,m :d ,,m | r ,,m :d ,,r :t, ,,r | d ,,r :m :— .f | r :r :s }

ing, praise the mer-cy that

‖— .f ,m :r :— .r | d :— :m | r ,,m :d ,,r :t, ,,r | d ,,r :m :— .f }

cresc.

— pro-longs thy Days; and sing ing, praise the

‖r :r :s | — .f ,m :r :— .r | d :— :— | r ,,m:f ,,s :l ,,t }

mf p

mer-cy that pro-longs thy Days.

p cresc.

d .,r :m .,f :s .,l | t, .,d :r .,m :f .,s | l ,t .d' :r :-.d | d :— :d .,m
mf più mosso
Hal-le-
mf
p
mf
più mosso
r :s, :r .,s | d .,r :m .,f :r .,d | t, :s, :d .,t, | l, .,d :t, .,r :d .,r
-lu - jah, Hal-le-lu - - - jah, Hal - - -
m .,f :fe :-.s | s :-.f :m .,r | d .,r :m .,f :s .,l | r .,m :f .,s :l .,ta
dim.
- le-lu - jah, Hal - - - -
dim.
l .,r :r :-.d | d :— :d .,m | r :s, :r .,s | d .,r :m .,f :r .,d
p
mf
- le-lu - jah, Hal - le - lu - jah, Hal - le - lu - - -
p
mf

cresc.
-jah, Hal - - le-lu - jah, Hal-
cresc.
- - - - - le-lu - jah,
mf
mf cresc.
Broadly
ff
Hal - le-lu - jah, Hal - le - lu - jah,
ff Broadly
p cresc.
Hal - - - - - le-
p cresc.

Marks of expression at no point to be interpreted literally.

61 NOW TO THE EARTH IN MERCY

(THE COMING OF JOY)

PERCY C. BUCK
reprinted by permission

Lento commodo (about ♩ = 60)

Key A mi.

p SOP.

1 Now to the earth in mer - cy a Sa - viour is giv - en,
2 Bring Him not gold, no splen - dour His king - dom re - quir - eth;

p ALTO

1 Now to the earth in mer - cy a Sa - viour is giv - en,
2 Bring Him not gold, no splen - dour His king - dom re - quir - eth;

p TEN.

1 Now to the earth in mer - cy a Sa - viour is giv - en,
2 Bring Him not gold, no splen - dour His king - dom re - quir - eth;

p BASS

1 Now to the earth in mer - cy a Sa - viour is giv - en,
2 Bring Him not gold, no splen - dour His king - dom re - quir - eth;

f F

C t

1. See! for a ran - som a Child is de - scend - ed from Hea - ven;
2. Nay! bring not frankincense, He no burnt of - f'rings de - sir - eth;

1. See! for a ran - som a Child is de scend - ed from Hea - ven;
2. Nay! bring not frank - incense, He no burnt of - f'rings de - sir - eth;

1. See! for a ran - som a Child is de - scended from Hea - ven;
2. Nay! bring not frankincense, He no burnt of - f'rings de - sir - eth;

1. See! for a ran - som a Child is de - scend - ed from Hea - ven;
2. Nay! bring not frank - in - cense, He no burnt of - f'rings de - sir - eth;

This anthem to be sung unaccompanied.

1. Kings bring Him pre-sents, and an-gels ex-tol Him with sing-ing,
2. Bring Him not myrrh, o-ver Him death hath no do-min- (Go to last line)
1. Kings bring Him pre-sents, and an-gels ex-tol Him with sing-ing,
2. Bring Him not myrrh, o-ver Him death hath no do-min- (Go to last line)
1. Kings bring Him pre-sents, and an-gels ex-tol Him with sing-ing,
2. Bring Him not myrrh, o-ver Him death hath no do-min- (Go to last line)
1. Kings bring Him pre-sents, and an-gels ex-tol Him with sing-ing,
2. Bring Him not myrrh, o-ver Him death hath no do-min- (Go to last line)
1st time
Rose of the world! for our joy from a Vir-gin up-spring-ing.
Rose of the world! for our joy from a Vir-gin up-spring-ing.
Rose of the world! for our joy from a Vir-gin up-spring-ing.
Rose of the world! from a Vir-gin up-spring-ing.
-a-tion; Throne of our love! we our hearts bring in pure ad-or-a-tion.
-a-tion; Throne of our love! we our hearts bring in pure ad-or-a-tion.
-a-tion; Throne of our love! we our hearts bring in pure ad-or-a-tion.
-a-tion; Throne of love! we our hearts bring in pure ad-or-a-tion.

62 O CHRIST WHO ART THE LIGHT AND DAY

CHRISTE QUI LUX ES ET DIES

Edited with an English Text by
R. R. TERRY

WILLIAM BYRD
(1543–1623)

♪ = 140

Mode ii
(Ray Mode transposed)

(To be sung quietly throughout)

O Christ who art the light and day, Thou dri-vest darksome night a-way.

We know Thee as the Light of light, Il-lu-mi-na-ting mor-tal sight.

VERSE 2 [Melody in Bass]

SOP. *(cresc.)* ALTO

All ho-ly Lord, we pray to Thee, Keep us to-night from dan-ger free, Grant us, dear Lord, in Thee to

TEN.

All ho-ly Lord, we pray to Thee, Keep us to-night from dan-ger free, Grant us, dear Lord, in Thee to

BAR.

BASS

To be sung unaccompanied

(pp)
rest, So be our sleep in quiet blest.
rest, So be our sleep in quiet blest.
VERSE 3 [Melody in Baritone]
Let not the temp - ter round us creep, With
(cresc.)
Let not the temp - ter round us creep, With
Let not the temp - ter round us creep, With
thoughts of e - vil while we sleep, Nor with his wiles the
thoughts of e - vil while we sleep, Nor with his wiles the

VERSE 4
[Melody in Tenor]
And make us in Thy sight im-pure.
flesh al - lure, And make us in Thy sight impure. And while the
flesh al - lure, And make us in Thy sight im-pure. And while the
(pp)
(cresc.)
eyes soft slum-ber take, Still be the heart to Thee a-wake,
eyes soft slum-ber take, Still be the heart to Thee a - wake,
(dim.)
Be Thy right hand up - held a-bove Thy ser - vants rest-ing
Be Thy right hand up - held a-bove Thy ser - vants rest-ing

VERSE 5 [Melody in Alto]
in Thy love. Yea, our De - fen-der, be Thou nigh To bid the
in Thy love. Yea, our De - fen-der, be Thou nigh To bid the
powers of dark-ness fly, Keep us from sin, and guide for good Thy
powers of dark-ness fly, Keep us from sin, and guide for good Thy
ser-vants pur - chased by Thy blood.
VERSE 6 [Melody in Sop.]
ser- vants pur-chased by Thy blood. Re - mem-ber
ser- vants pur-chased by Thy blood. Re - mem-ber

us, dear Lord, we pray, While in this mor-tal flesh we stay;
us, dear Lord, we pray, While in this mor-tal flesh we stay;
(cresc).
(f)
'Tis Thou who dost the soul de-fend, Be pre-sent
'Tis Thou who dost the soul de-fend, Be pre-sent
doh is B
(p
with us to the end. A - men.
with us to the end. A - men.

63 O GLADSOME LIGHT, O GRACE

Translated from the Greek by
ROBERT BRIDGES
(1844–1930)

LOUIS BOURGEOIS (1549)
Set by CLAUD GOUDIMEL (1565)
Edited by HENRY G. LEY

Moderato e sostenuto

Key F

SOP. ALTO TEN. BASS

1. O gladsome light, O grace Of God the Fa-ther's face,
Th'e-ter-nal splendour wear-ing; Ce-les-tial, ho-ly, blest,
Our Saviour Je-sus Christ, Joy-ful in Thine ap-pear-ing.

2. Now ere day fa-deth quite, We see the eve-ning light,

This anthem may be sung unaccompanied.

Reprinted by permission from the "Yattendon Hymnal."

Our wont-ed hymn out-pour - ing. Fa - ther of might un-known,
Thee, His in-car-nate Son, And Ho-ly Spi-rit a - dor - ing.
3. To Thee of right be - longs All praise of ho-ly songs,
O Son of God, life-giv - er; Thee, therefore, O Most High,
The world doth glori - fy, And shall ex-alt for ev - er. A - men.

64

O GOD OF BETHEL

Adapted to Words by PHILIP DODDRIDGE (1702–51)

CHRISTOPHER TYE (c.1508–72)

wea - ry pil - grim-age Hast all our fa - thers led:
pil - grim-age Hast all our fa - thers led:
-age Hast all our fa - - thers led:
-age Hast all our fa - thers led, our fa - thers led:
p
pp
poco cresc.
Our vows and prayers we now pre - sent Be - fore Thy
Our vows and prayers we now pre - sent Be - fore Thy
Our vows and prayers we now pre - sent Be - fore Thy
Our vows and prayers we now pre - sent Be - fore Thy

sempre cresc.
throne of grace; God of our fa - thers,
sempre cresc.
throne of grace; God of our fa - thers, God of our
sempre cresc.
throne of grace; God of our fa - thers, God of our fa - thers
sempre cresc.
throne of grace; God of our fa - thers, God of our fa - thers,
sempre cresc.
dim. e rall.
pp
be the God Of their suc - ceed - ing race.
dim. e rall.
pp
fa-thers, be the God Of their suc - ceed - ing race.
dim. e rall.
pp
be the God Of their suc - ceed - ing race.
dim. e rall.
pp
be the God Of their suc - ceed - ing race.
dim. e rall.
pp

65 O GOD, THOU FAITHFUL GOD

From CANTATA Nº 24

JOHANN HEERMANN (1585-1647)
Tr. CATHERINE WINKWORTH, (1829-78)

JOHANN SEBASTIAN BACH
(1685-1750)

Andante moderato
Key D mi.
mf
SOPRANO
ALTO
1. O___ God, Thou faith - ful God,
2. If___ dan - gers ga - ther round,
TENOR
BASS
Andante moderato
(mp)
Thou foun - tain ev - er
Still keep___ me___ calm and

r :— |d :
l, :t, |s, :
flow - ing;
fear - less;
f :r |m :
f .r :s .s, |d :
:m |m :f .s ,l |s :f |m :
:d |d :d .r |t, .d :d .t, |d :
With - out whom no - thing is,
Help me to bear the cross
:s |l :l .f |f .m :r .s |s :
:d .t, |l, .s, :f, |s, :s, |d, :

All — per - fect
When life — is
gifts be - stow - ing; A
dark and cheer - less; To

pure and health - y frame. O
o - ver - come my foe. With
give me, and with - in.
words and ac - tions kind;
Cmi.
Cmaj.3

A con - science free from blame,
When coun - sel I would know,
(dim.)

A soul un - hurt by sin.
Good coun - sel let me find.

Fᵗ d f ,r .r ,f :(l,)r |m :m |r .m,f :r |d :—

dim. *p poco rall. al fine*

:(fe)t, |d :d |d .t,,l :t, .t, |d : .d ,ta

A soul un - hurt by sin. A
Good coun - sel let me find. Good

:(r)s |s :l |l .t ,d' :t r |m : .d

dim. *p poco rall. al fine*

:(r)s, |d .t, :l, .s, |f, .r, :s, |d :—

sin.
find.

dim. *p poco rall. al fine*

|— :— |— :— |— . : | :

l, :s, |f, :— .s, |s, . : | :

soul un - hurt by sin.
coun - sel let me find.

f :m |r :— .m |m . : | :

|— :— |— :— |— . : | :

rit.

66

O LORD GOD

SET FOR SOPRANO VOICES

Book of Common Prayer, 1661

PERCY C. BUCK

Lento, molto espress.

Key B♭ mi

VOICE

ORGAN

p SOLO

O Lord God, who seest that we put not our trust in anything that we do; Merciful-ly grant that by Thy power we may be de-fend-ed against all ad-ver-si-ty; through

senza Ped.

Ped.

f E♭ mi.

B♭ mi.

Je - sus Christ our Lord.
senza Ped.
p CHORUS
O Lord God, who se - est that we
Ped.
put not our trust in anything that we do; Merciful -ly
senza Ped.
grant that by Thy power we may be de - fend - ed against all ad -

SOP. I.
-ver-si-ty; through Je - - sus Christ,
SOP. II.
-ver-si-ty; through Je - - sus Christ our
Ped.
— Je - sus Christ our Lord.
Lord, Je - sus Christ our Lord.
senza Ped.
SOLO
A - men, A - men.
A - men, A - - men.
A - men, A - - men.
Ped.

67 O LORD, INCREASE MY FAITH

ORLANDO GIBBONS
(1583-1625)

This anthem to be sung unaccompanied.

Emi.t

p

en - due mewith wisdom, with wis - dom,

wis-dom, with wis - dom, en - due__ me with wis - dom, cha-

-due mewith wis - dom, cha - ri - ty,

p

en - due mewith wis - dom, cha-

cresc.

cha - ri - ty, cha - ri - ty, and pa-

cresc.

-ri - ty, cha - ri - ty, and pa - tience, and pa -

cresc.

cha - ri - ty, and pa - tience, and pa -

cresc.

-ri - ty, cha - ri - ty, and pa -

cresc.

smoothly
tience, in all my ad-ver - si-
tience, in all my ad-ver - si-
tience, in all my ad-ver-si - ty, in all my ad-ver - si-
tience, in all my ad-ver-si - ty, ad - ver - si -
-ty. Sweet Je - su, say A - men, sweet
-ty. Sweet Je - su, say A-men, sweet Je-su, say A-
-ty. Sweet Je - su, say A-men, sweet
-ty. Sweet Je - su, say A - men, sweet

4 E mi. f A mi.

Je-su, say A - men, sweet Je - su, say A -

-men A - men, sweet Je - su, say A-men,

Je - su, say A - men,

Je-su, say A - men,

p dim. e rall. *pp*

-men, sweet Je - su, say A - men.

sweet Je - su, say A - men, say A-men.

sweet Je - su, say— A - men, say— A - men.

sweet Je - su, say A - men,— A - men, A - men.

dim. e rall. *pp*

68 O LORD, MY GOD

(SOLOMON'S PRAYER)

This anthem may be sung unaccompanied.

place, And when Thou hear - est, Lord, for-give,
place, And when Thou hear - est, Lord, for - give,
place, And when Thou hear - est, for-give,
G mi.
Hear Thou in Heav'n Thy dwell - ing place, And when Thou
mf
hear - est, Lord, for - give, And when Thou
dim.
p
hear - est, Lord, for - give, for-give, for-

*This may be substituted for the foregoing three bars if sung with restraint.

69 O LORD, MY GOD TO THEE

From Psalms xxv & xxvii

Attributed to
JACQUES ARCADELT
(1490-1556)

Andante

O Lord my God to Thee do I lift up my soul. O Lord in Thee, in Thee have I trust-ed. Let me not be a-sham-ed, Let not my foes tri-umph o-ver me. O lead me in a plain

This anthem may be sung unaccompanied.

path; cast me not off nei - ther for-sake — me. Teach me Thy
way, Lord, Lead me, lead me in a plain path. O
hide not Thy face, Hide not Thy face far from me. Lord God,
Lord God, Hide not Thy face far from me. A - men.
Slow
Slow

70 O LORD, SUPPORT US

By permission from Curwen Edition No. 80595, published by J. Curwen & Sons Ltd. 24, Berners Street, London W. 1.

This anthem may be sung unaccompanied.

mf
work done. Then, Lord, in Thy mer - cy,
mf

poco rit.
dim.
grant us safe lodg - ing, a ho - ly rest, and
dim.

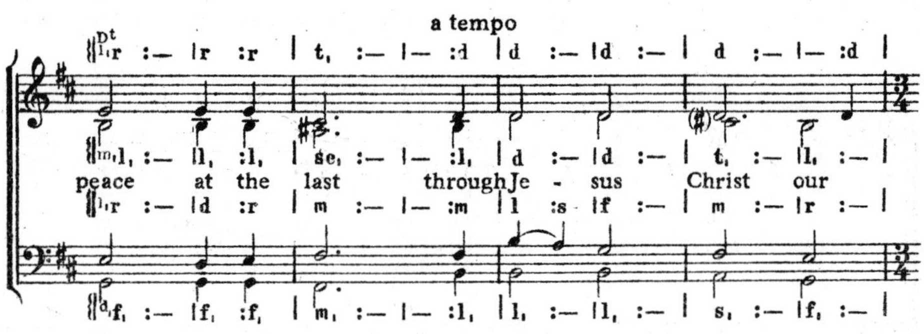
a tempo
peace at the last through Je - sus Christ our

A - - - men.
mf
f
mf
A - - - men.
Lord.
A - - - men.
mf
f
mf
A - - - men, A - men.

71 O LORD THE MAKER OF ALL THING

Words from the King's Primer. 1545

WILLIAM MUNDY
d. 1591 (?)
Edited by E. H. FELLOWES

Smoothly, with movement. ♩ = about 96

Key F♯ mi.

SOP. O Lord, the ma - ker of all thing,
ALTO O Lord, the ma - ker of all thing, We
TEN. O Lord, the ma-ker of all thing, We pray Thee
BASS O Lord, the ma-ker of all thing, We

SOP. We pray Thee now in this eve - ning
ALTO pray Thee now in this eve - ning
TEN. now in this eve - ning Us to de - fend through Thy
BASS pray Thee now in this eve - ning Us to de -

SOP. Us to de - fend through Thy mer - cy
ALTO Us to de - fend through Thy mer - cy From
TEN. mer - cy, Thy mer - cy, From all de - ceit of our
BASS - fend through Thy mer - cy, through Thy mer - cy From all de -

Reprinted from the Tudor Church Music Series (Oxford University Press.) *by permission.*

This anthem should be sung without accompaniment.

From all de-ceit of our e - ne-my, of our e - ne-my;

:m |s :f |m :m .r |de se :-.se |se :se .se |l :-.l |se :- | :d

r :d |t, :l, |— :se, |m :-.m |m :m .m |m :-.m |m :- | l,

all de-ceit of our e - ne-my, of our e - ne-my;

e - ne - my, our e - ne - my, of our e - ne-my; Let

t, :d |r :r |t, :m |t :— |t :t |d' :-.d' |t :- | :m

s, :l, .l, |s, :r, |m, :— |m :— |m :m |l, :-.l, |m :- | l,

- ceit of our e - ne - - my, of our e - ne-my;

f :-.f |m :r |r :de |r :r |f :-.m |r :d |d :t,

d :-.d |d :t, |l, :-.s, |fe, :l, |l, :-.s, |f, :m, |s, :-.f,

nei-ther us de - lud - ed be, Good Lord, with dream or fan-ta -

l :-.l |s :f |m :m |r :r |r :r |l, :d |r :-.r

f, :-.f, |d :s, |l, :l, |r, :r, |r, :-.m, |f, .s, :l, |s, :-.s,

d :d :m |s :-.s :f |m :r |de :m |m :-.r

cresc. *dim.*

m, :s, :d |t, :-.t, :d |d :l, |l, :d |d :d

- sy, Our heart wak-ing in Thee Thou keep, That we in

d :m :s |s :-.s :l |s :f |m :l |s :-.f

cresc. *dim.*

d, :d :d |m :-.m :l, |d :r |l, :l, |d :d

d :t, |l, :l, |se, :- | :t, |d :-.d |t, :l, |l, :se, |l, :- | :l,

pp *mf*

s, :s, |m, :m, |m, :- | :s, |m, :-.f, |s, :f, |m, :m, |m, :— |— :—

sin fall not on sleep, that we in sin fall not on sleep. O

m r |d :d |t, :- | :m |d :-.d |r :r |t, :t, |de :— |— :—

pp

d :s, |l, :l, |m, :- | :m, |l, :-.l, |s, :r, |m, :m, |l, :— |— :—

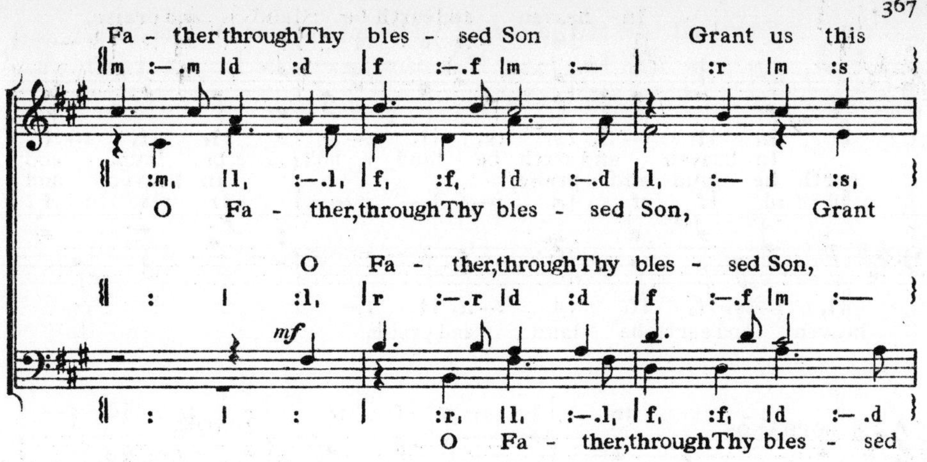
Fa - ther through Thy bles - sed Son Grant us this
O Fa - ther, through Thy bles - sed Son, Grant
O Fa - ther, through Thy bles - sed Son,
mf
O Fa - ther, through Thy bles - sed

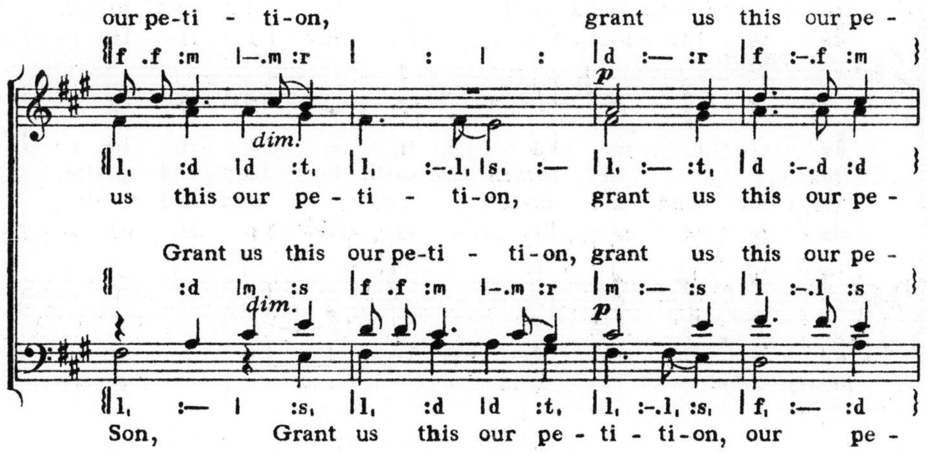
our pe-ti - ti-on, grant us this our pe -
p
dim.
us this our pe - ti - ti-on, grant us this our pe -
Grant us this our pe-ti - ti-on, grant us this our pe -
dim.
p
Son, Grant us this our pe - ti - ti-on, our pe -

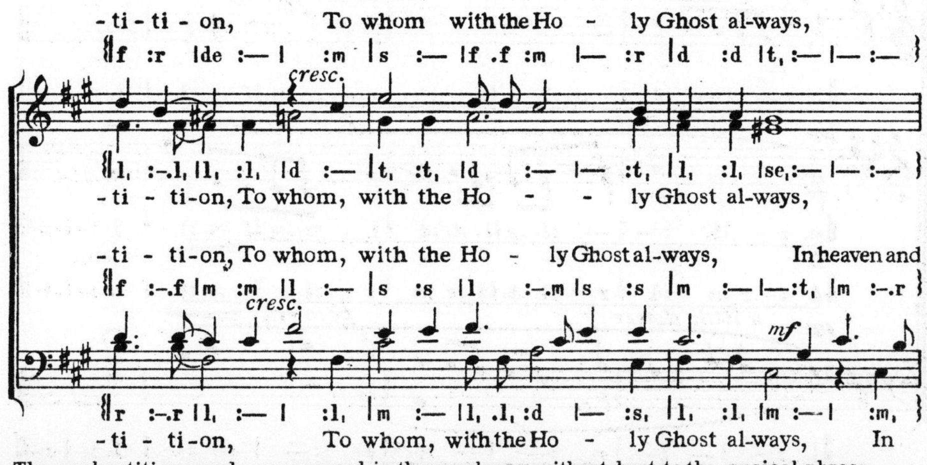
- ti - ti - on, To whom with the Ho - ly Ghost al-ways,
cresc.
- ti - ti-on, To whom, with the Ho - - ly Ghost al-ways,
- ti - ti-on, To whom, with the Ho - ly Ghost al-ways, In heaven and
cresc.
mf
- ti - ti-on, To whom, with the Ho - ly Ghost al-ways, In

The word petition may be pronounced in the usual way without hurt to the musical phrase.

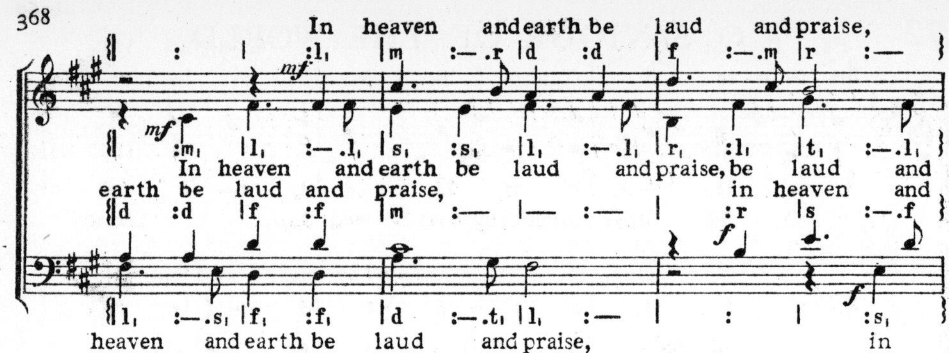
In heaven and earth be laud and praise,
mf
mf
In heaven and earth be laud and praise, be laud and
earth be laud and praise, in heaven and
f
f
heaven and earth be laud and praise, in

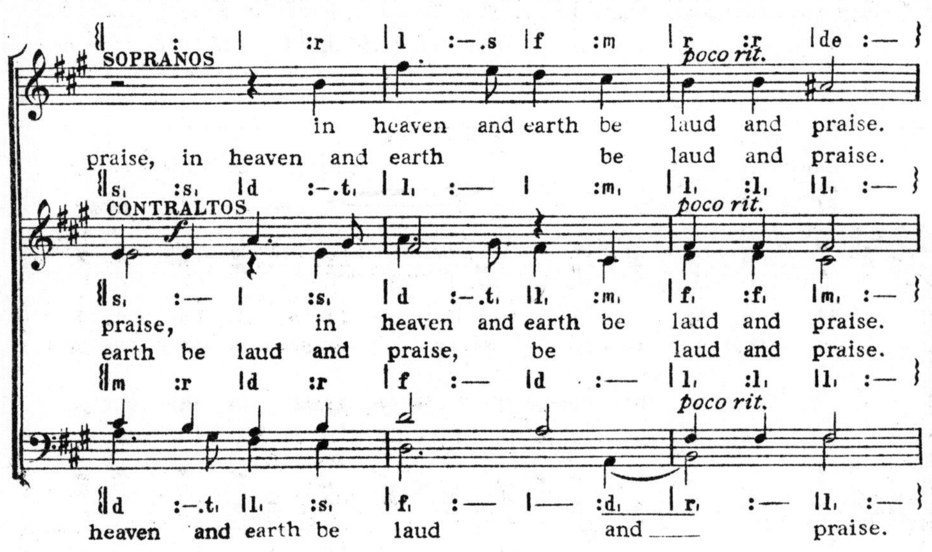
SOPRANOS
poco rit.
in heaven and earth be laud and praise.
praise, in heaven and earth be laud and praise.
CONTRALTOS
f
poco rit.
praise, in heaven and earth be laud and praise.
earth be laud and praise, be laud and praise.
poco rit.
heaven and earth be laud and praise.

pp
a little slower
poco rit.
A - - - - - - - - - - - - - - men.
a little slower
poco rit.
pp
A - - - - - - - - - - - - - - men.
a little slower
poco rit.
pp

72 O SAVIOUR OF THE WORLD

This Anthem may be sung unaccompanied. Small notes refer to organ part.

E♭ mi
E♭ maj.3
mf
cre - scen - do
f
dim.
world, O Sa-viour, Who by Thy Cross and pre-cious Blood hast re -
mf
cre - scen - do
f
dim.
Ped.

p
-deem - ed us, Save us, and help us, we hum-bly be-seech Thee, O
p

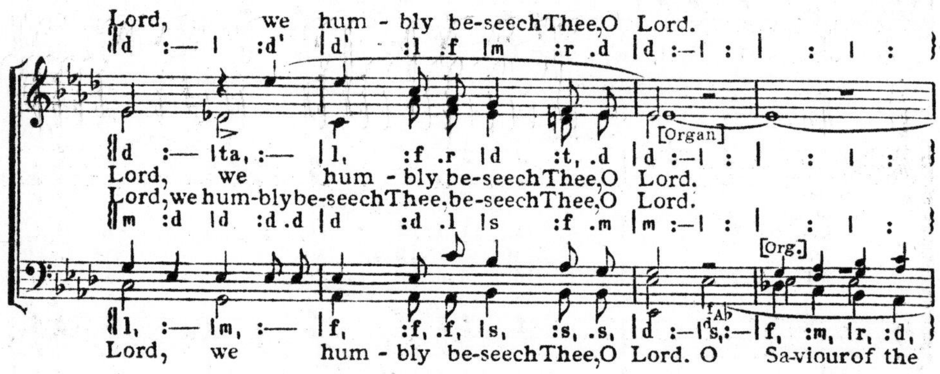

Lord, we hum - bly be-seech Thee, O Lord.
[Organ]
Lord, we hum - bly be-seech Thee, O Lord.
Lord, we hum-bly be-seech Thee, be-seech Thee, O Lord.
[Org.]
A♭
Lord, we hum - bly be-seech Thee, O Lord. O Sa-viour of the

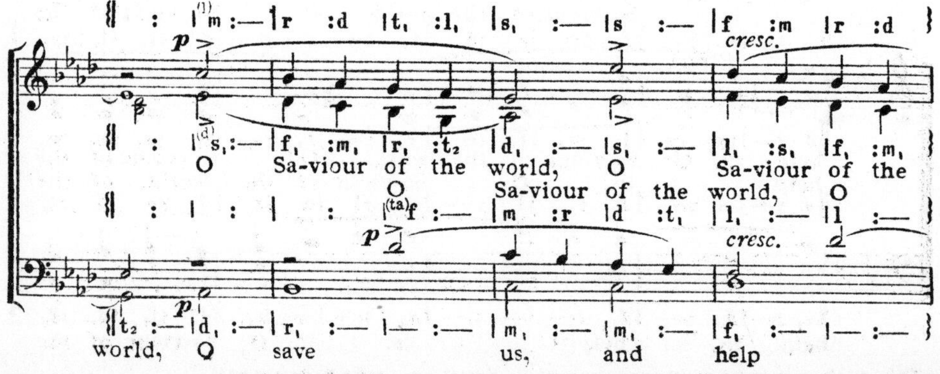

p
cresc.
O Sa-viour of the world, O Sa-viour of the
O Sa-viour of the world, O
p
cresc.
p
world, O save us, and help

sf
cre - scen - do al
world, O Sa - viour, Who by Thy Cross and pre-cious
Sa - viour of the world, Who by Thy Cross and pre-cious
sf
cre - scen - do al
us, O Sa - viour, Who by Thy Cross and pre-cious
Save us, and help us, we
f
p
Blood hast re-deem - ed us, Save us, and help us, we
Blood hast re-deem - ed us, Save us, and help us, we
f
p
hum-bly be-seech Thee, O Lord, O Sa-viour of the world, Save us, and
sf
pp
hum-bly be-seech Thee, O Lord, O save us, Save us, and
sf
pp
Rather slower
help us, we hum-bly be-seech Thee, O Lord. A - men.
p
cresc.
dim.
help us, we hum-bly be-seech Thee, O Lord. A - men, A - men.
cresc
p
dim.
Ped.
help us, we hum-bly be-seech Thee, O Lord. A - men.

73 O SAVIOUR OF THE WORLD

Collect for the visitation of the sick.

GIOVANNI PERLUIGI SANTI DA PALESTRINA
1525-94

This anthem may be sung unaccompanied.

pp
poco cresc.
mf
of the world, Who by Thy Cross and pre - cious Blood
of the world, Who by Thy Cross and pre - cious Blood
of the world, Who by Thy Cross and pre - cious Blood
of the world, Who by Thy Cross and pre - cious Blood
dim.
p
hast re-deem - ed, re - deem - ed us; Save
hast re-deem - ed, re - deem - ed us; Save
hast re-deem - ed, re - deem - ed us; Save
hast re-deem - ed, re - deem - ed us; Save

mp
— us and help us, we be-seech
— us and help us, we be - seech
— us and help us, we be-seech
— us and help us, we be - seech
mp
dim. e rall. al fine
pp
Thee, we hum - bly be-seech Thee, O Lord.
Thee, we hum - bly be - seech Thee, O Lord.
Thee, we hum - bly be - seech Thee, O Lord.
Thee, we hum - bly be - seech Thee, O Lord.
dim. e rall. al fine
pp

74 O THAT I KNEW WHERE I MIGHT FIND HIM!

Job xxiii. 3, 8-9;
St. John xx. 29.

W. STERNDALE BENNETT
(1816-75)

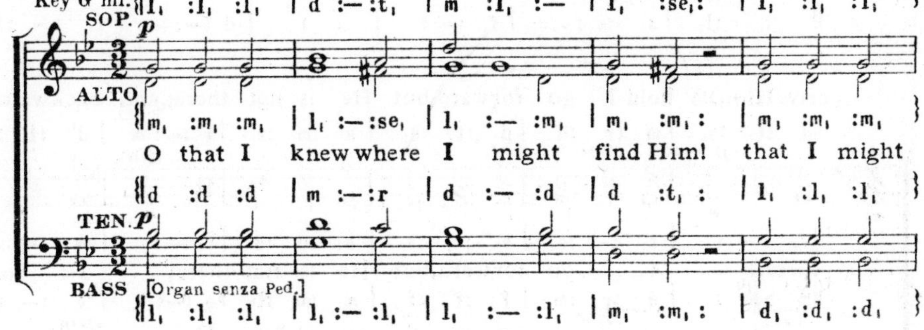

Key G mi.
SOP.
ALTO
O that I knew where I might find Him! that I might
TEN.
BASS [Organ senza Ped.]

cresc.
come e - ven to His seat! O that I knew where I might
cresc.

to His seat! Be - hold, I go
dim.
cresc.
find Him! that I might come e - ven to His seat!
dim.
Ped.

This anthem may be sung unaccompanied. Small notes refer to the organ.

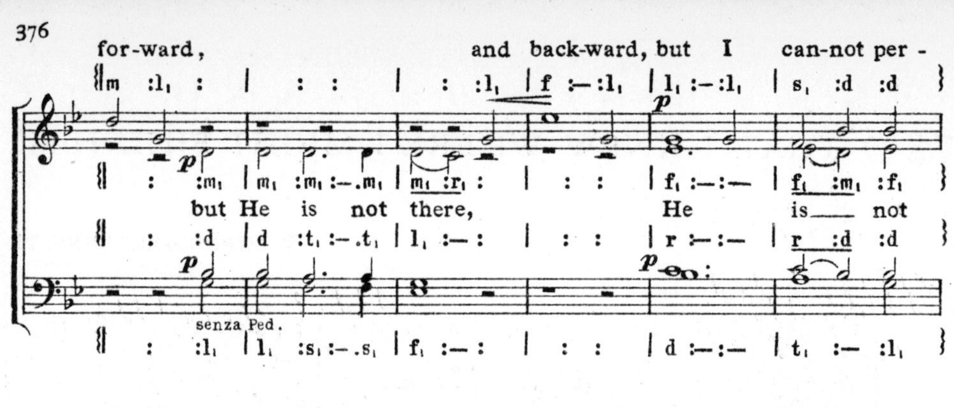
for-ward, and back-ward, but I can-not per -
but He is not there, He is___ not
senza Ped.

- ceive Him, Be hold I go forward, but He is not there; and backward,
cresc.
dim.
there, I___ go forward, but He is not there; I go
Ped.
senza Ped.

but I can-not per - ceive Him, I can - not per- ceive
dim.
for-ward, but I can-not, I can - not___ per - ceive
Ped.

Him: On the left hand where He doth work, on the left hand
senza Ped.

NOTE: A very short silence may well be left before the words **'He hideth Himself'**

Arioso moderato (𝅗𝅥=72)

pp *p*

— the right hand. Bless-ed are they, are they that have not

— the right hand. Bless-ed are they, are they that have not

— the right hand. Bless-ed are they, are they that have not

— the right hand. Bless - ed are they ———

Arioso moderato (𝅗𝅥=72)

pp *p*

Ped.

cresc. *f*

seen, that have not seen, and yet have be-liev - ed, Bless - ed

seen, that have not seen, and yet have be-liev - ed, Bless-ed,

seen, that have not seen, not seen, and yet have be-liev - ed, Bless -

— that have not seen, not seen, and yet have be - liev - ed, Bless-ed,

cresc. *f*

bless - ed are they that have not seen, that have not seen, not seen, and
blessed are they that have not seen, not seen, and yet have be-
-ed are they that have not seen, and
bless - ed are they that have not seen, they that have not seen, and
D.𝄋 E mi.
yet have be - liev - ed. Bless - ed are they that have not
liev - ed. Bless - ed are they that have not
yet have be - liev - ed. Bless - ed are they, they that have not
yet have be - liev - ed. Bless - ed are they, are
D.𝄋

seen, that have not, not
seen, are they that have not seen, that have not
seen, are they that have not seen, that have not
they, are they that have not seen, that have not
senza Ped.
seen, that have not seen, and yet have be - liev - ed,
seen, that have not seen, and yet have be - liev - ed,
seen, that have not seen, and yet have be - liev - ed,
seen, that have not seen, and yet have be - liev -
Ped

A mi.
Bless - ed, bless - ed are they that have not seen, that
Bless-ed, bless-ed, bless - ed are
Bless - - ed, bless - ed are
- ed, Bless- ed are they, are they that have not
G t
have not seen, and yet have be - liev - ed, that
they, and yet, and yet have be liev - -
they that have not seen, and yet have be - liev - ed, that
seen, and yet have be - liev - - ed, that
senza Ped.

have not seen, that have not, have not
-ed, that have not seen, and yet, yet
have not seen, have not seen, and yet have be -
have not seen, have not seen, and yet have be -
seen, and yet have be - liev - ed, that have
have be - liev - - ed, have not seen, not
-liev - - ed, that have not seen, that have not
liev - - ed, yet have be - liev -
Ped

— not seen, not seen, and yet, —
seen, that — have not — seen, — not seen, and yet —
seen, that have not seen, and yet, —
-ed, that have not seen, that have not seen, that
— and yet have, — yet have be - liev - ed.
— have, — yet have be liev - ed.
— and yet — have, — yet have be - liev - ed.
have not seen, not seen, yet have be - liev - ed.

75 O WHAT THEIR JOY AND THEIR GLORY MUST BE

Translated from the Latin of Abelard
by J. M. NEALE

WILLIAM H. HARRIS

From the Oxford Series of Modern Anthems. Reprinted by permission.
Founded on a French Melody

Those end - less Sab -
-baths the bless - ed ones see!
Crown for the va -

-liant; to wea - ry ones rest;
cresc.
ff
God shall be all, and in all ev - er
blest.

What are the Mon - arch, his court,
What are the Mon - arch, his court, his court
What are the Mon - arch, his court
What are the Mon - arch, his court
and his throne? What are the
and his throne? What are the peace, what are the
and his throne? What are the peace, the
and his throne? What are the peace, the
mf

f :— | m :m | m :r | m :s | fe :—
peace and the joy that they own?
l, :— .t, | d :t, | l, :r | d :t, .d | r :— .d
peace and the joy that they own, they
l :— | l :se | l :— | — :s | l :—
peace and the joy they own?
m :r | l, .d :m .r | d :t, | d .r :m | r :—
peace and the joy that they own?
s :— | d :— | t, :d | l, :— | s, :s,
mf
Tell us, ye blest ones, that
t, :s, | d :— | t, :d | l, :— | s, :
mf
own? Tell us, ye blest ones,
s :— | : | : | : | :
s, :— | : | s, :— | f, :l, | r :— .t,
p espress.
Tell us, ye blest

in it have share, If
If what ye
Tell If what ye feel,
ones, Tell if
what ye feel, ye can ful - ly de -
feel, ye feel, ye can ful - ly de -
ye feel, ye can ful - ly de -
what ye feel, ye can ful - ly de -

-clare.
-clare.
-clare.
-clare.
dim.
Tru - ly 'Je -
Tru - ly
Tru - ly 'Je - ru - -
Tru - ly 'Je - ru - sa - lem' name

-ru - sa-lem' name we that shore, 'Vi - -
name we that shore,
- - sa-lem' name we that shore, 'Vi -
we, name we that shore,
-sion of peace' that brings joy ev - er -
'Vi - sion that brings joy ev - er -
- sion of peace' that brings joy ev - er -
'Vi - sion of peace' that brings joy ev-er-

cresc.
-more! Wish and ful - fil - ment
-more! Wish and ful - fil - -
-more! Wish and ful - fil - -
-more! Wish and ful - fil - -
Nor
can se - - - vered be ne'er,
-ment can se - - - vered be ne'er,
-ment can se - vered be ne'er, Nor
-ment can se - - - vered be ne'er, Nor

— the thing—

|s :— .s |f :m |s :l |s :s |s :— |m :f

dim.

|(d') s :— |d :d |m :r |r :r |m :— |d :r

Nor the thing prayed for come short of the

dim.

|(s) r :d |d :d |t, :l, |t, :t, |t, :— |l, :l,

Nor — the thing prayed for come short of the

|t :s |l :s |s :r |r :r |s :— |l :r

dim.

— the thing— prayed for come short of the

|— :m |l, :d |m, :f, |s, .l, :s, .f, |m, :— |l, :f,

dim.

— the thing— prayed for— come short of the

|r :— |d f :— | r' :—.d' :l .t |d' :—.r',m' :f' d'

E is ray t

unis.

prayer. —

|t, :— |d f :— | : : | : :

prayer. —

|s :— |m l :— | : : | : :

prayer. —

|s, :— |l, r :— | : : | : :

prayer. —

SOLO

p

dolce espress.

*Lento
G mi.
We, where no trouble dis-traction can
We, where no trouble dis-traction can
We, where no trouble dis-traction can
We, where no trouble dis-traction can
Lento
pp
espr.
bring, Safe - ly the an - thems of— Si - on— shall sing;
bring, the— an - thems, the an - thems of— Si - on— shall sing;
bring, Safe - ly the an - thems of Si - on— shall sing;
bring, the an - thems of Si - on shall sing;
espr.

* From * to * (p. 397) may be sung by a semichorus.

cresc.
While for Thy grace, Lord, their voi-ces of praise Thy bles-sed
cresc.
cresc.

peo - ple shall ev - er - more raise.
mf
dim.

pp
There—dawns no Sabbath, no Sabbath is o'er,
pp
mistico
p
Those Sabbath keep-ers have one, and no more;
cresc.
One and un - end- ing is
cresc.

cresc.
cresc.
C♯mi.
is that tri - umph song Which to the An - gels
Which to the
cresc.
p
p
that tri - umph song Which to the An - gels
Gt.
Sw.
p
Gt.
Sw.
which to the An-gels
An-gels
and us shall be - long.
p
rit.

A tempo primo
Now in the mean-while, with hearts raised on high, We for that
pp
A tempo primo
coun - try must yearn and must sigh, Seek - ing Je - ru - sa - lem,
p
dear na - tive land, Through our long ex - ile on Ba - by-lon's

strand.
r :d
r :d
(tempo ad lib.)
(Sw.)
accel.
Gt.
E mi.
d .m :s .f
l .,l :t
l
Low be-fore Him,
a tempo
più f

Maestoso molto

l .,l :t | d' :— | — :-. | d' .,t :l .s ,f | m :d .d | f :m .r

allarg. ***ff***

d .,d :r | m :— | — :-. | d :d .r | m :d .d | f :m .r

Low be fore Him, Low be - fore Him with our prais - es we

d' .,d' :d' | d' :— | — :-. | d :d .r | m :d .d | f :m .r

allarg.

m .,m :f | m :— | — :-. | d :d .r | m :d .d | f :m .r

Maestoso molto

allarg.

r :d | s :m .d | f :m .m | m .r :m .s | fe t :d'

B mi.

r :d | s, :m .d | f :m .m | m .r :m .s, | fe t, :d

fall, Of whom, and in whom, and through whom are all;

r :d | s :m .d | f :m .m | m .r :m .s | fe t :d'

r :d | s :m .d | f :m .m | m .r :m .s | fe t :d'

: | f :m .f | r :d .d | f :s .l | l m :r

E mi.

allarg.

: | f :m .f | r :d .d | f :s .l | l m :r

Of whom the Fa - ther, and through whom the Son

: | f :m .f | r :d .d | f :s .l | l m :r

allarg.

: | f :m .f | r :d .d | f :s .l | l m :r

3

allarg.

Pedal reed

3

A - - - men,
a tempo
A - men, A-
In whom the Spi - rit, with these ev - er One.
A - - men
a tempo
A - -
a tempo
A - - men, A - men, A - men.
allarg.
- - - men, A - - - men, A - men, A - men.
A - men, A - - men A - men A - men.
allarg.
- - men, A - - - men, A - men, A - men.
allarg.

76 REJOICE IN THE LORD ALWAY

SOPRANO VOICES ONLY

Philippians IV. vv 4-7

HENRY G. LEY

From 'Six Short Anthems' Oxford University Press

poco rit.
and a-gain I say, re-joice.
poco rit.
poco rit.
a tempo
mf a little slower
Let your moder - a-tion be known unto all men, be known un - to
Let your moder - a-tion be known unto
mf a little slower
cre - - scen - do ff
all men, The Lord is at hand, the Lord is at
cre - - scen - do ff
cresc.

G maj.
SOLO or a few voices
hand. Be
rit.
Andante con espressione
B mi.
care - ful for nothing, be care - ful for nothing, but in ev - erything by
Andante con espressione
Sw.
senza Ped.
A mi.
prayer and sup - pli - ca - tion, with thanks-giv-ing, let your re -

A maj.
rit.
p CHORUS
-quests be made known un-to God, and the peace of
rit.
a tempo tranquillo
mf
Sw.
Gt.
Sw.
pp
Ped.
Eb
pp rit.
slowly
God which pass-eth all un-der-
fD
p
pp rit.
slowly
and the peace of God which pass-eth all un-der-
slowly
G mi.
fEb
mf a tempo
-standing shall keep your hearts and minds, shall keep your hearts and
mf a tempo
a tempo
Gt.

pp molto rit.
minds through Christ Je - sus, through Christ Je - sus.
pp molto rit.
pp Sw.
molto rit.
rit.
Sw.
Man.
Tranquillo
p
A - - - men, A - - - - - - men,
p
A - - - - -
Tranquillo
p
Sw.
Ped.
molto rit.
a tempo
pp
A - - - - men.
molto rit.
a tempo
pp
- men, A - - - - men.
molto rit.
a tempo
Sw.
Ch.
pp
ppp
Sw.

77 REJOICE IN THE LORD ALWAY

ANTHEM FOR THREE SOLO VOICES AND CHORUS

Known as **'THE BELL ANTHEM'**

Philippians iv. 4-7

HENRY PURCELL
1658-95

VERSE

{:d |s :-.f :m |f :r :— |s :— :l .,m |f :— :r |m :d :— }

f ALTO

Re - joice in the Lord al - way, and a - gain I say, re - -

{:d' |m' :-.r' :d' |r' :t :— |d' :— :m' .,m' |r' :— :s |s :-.l :fe }

f TENOR

Re - joice in the Lord al - way, and a - gain I say,___ re -

{:d |d' :-.t :d' |f :s :— |m :— :de .,de |r :— :t, |d :l, :— }

f BASS

Re - joice in the Lord al - way, and a - gain I say, re - -

f

{|t, :— :r |s :-.f :m |l :f :— |r :-:s .,r |m :-.f :s |f :r :— |d :— :d }

-joice. Re - joice in the Lord al - way, and a - gain___ I say, re - joice. Re -

p

{|s :— :t |t :-.t :de' |r' :l :-.t .,d' |t :-:r' .,r' |s :— :d' |r' :t :— |d' :— :d' }

-joice. Re - joice in the Lord al - - way, and a - gain I say, re - joice. Re -

p

{|s, :— :s |m :-.m :l |f :r :— |s :-:t, .,t, |d :-.r :m |f :s :— |d :— :d }

-joice. Re - joice in the Lord al - way, and a - gain___ I say, re - joice. Re -

p

*

p

*The original Symphonies may be played here, see Purcell Society's Edition. [Ed.]

-joice in the Lord al - way, and a-gain I say, re - joice. Re-joice in the
-joice in the Lord al - way, and a-gain I say, — re-joice. Re-joice in the
-joice in the Lord al - way, and a-gain I say, re - joice. Re-joice in the
Lord al - way, and a-gain — I say, re - joice.
Lord al - way, and a-gain I say, re - joice.
Lord al - way, and a-gain — I say, — re-joice.
mf

Let your mod-er-a - tion be
Let your mod-er - a - tion be known un - to all men, be
Let your mod-er-a - tion be known, be
known un - to all men. The Lord is at hand, the Lord is at
known un - to all men. The Lord is at hand, the Lord is at
known un - to all men. The Lord is at hand, the Lord is at

CHORUS
SOPRANO ff
hand. Re - joice in the Lord al - way, and a - gain — I say, re -
CHORUS
D mi.
SOLI
CHORUS
-joice. Re - joice in the Lord al - way, and a - gain, a - gain, a -
SOLI
CHORUS
-gain I say, re - joice, and a - gain, a - gain I — say, re -

*The original Symphony may again replace this three-bar interlude.

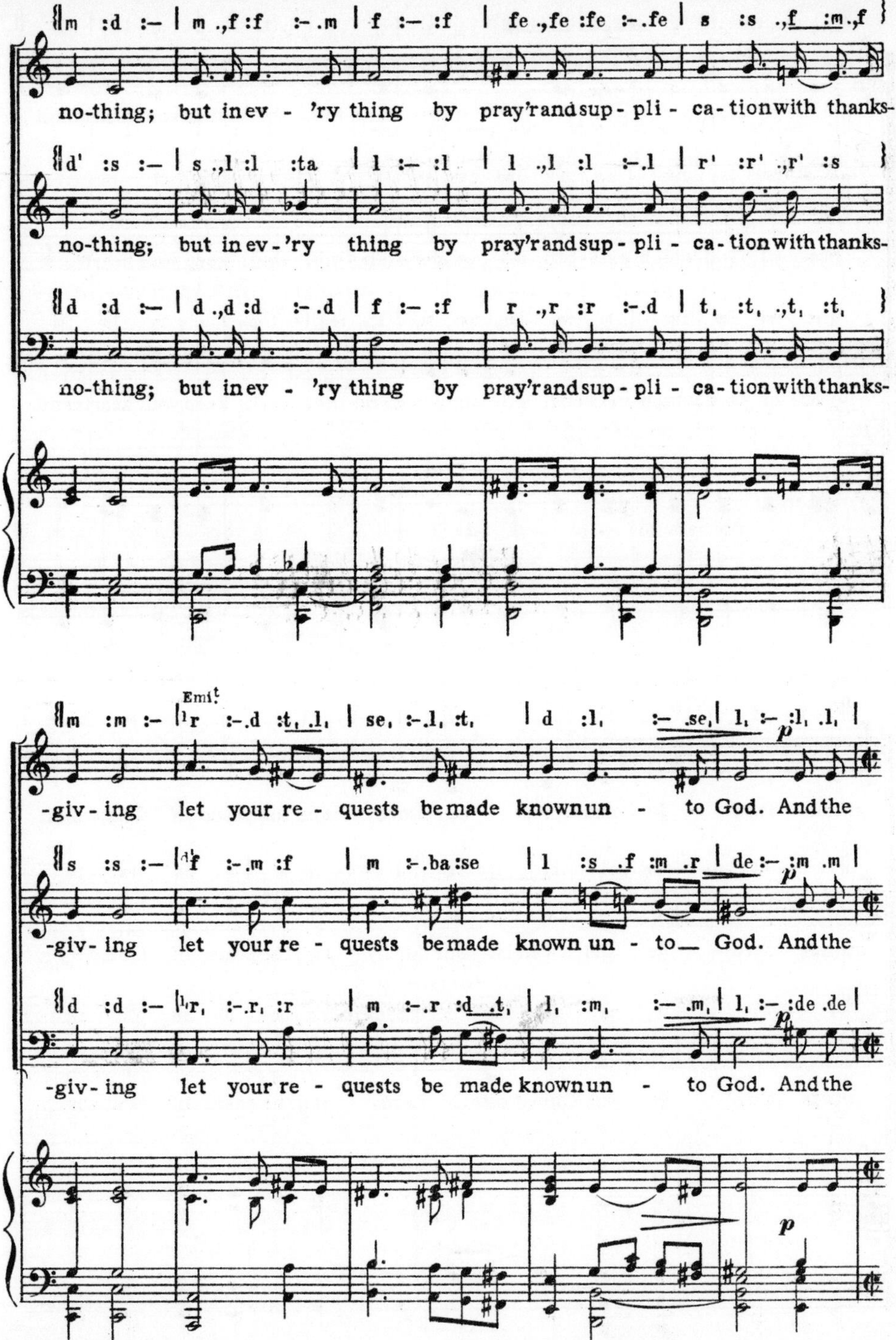
no-thing; but in ev - 'ry thing by pray'r and sup - pli - ca - tion with thanks-
no-thing; but in ev - 'ry thing by pray'r and sup - pli - ca - tion with thanks-
no-thing; but in ev - 'ry thing by pray'r and sup - pli - ca - tion with thanks-
-giv - ing let your re - quests be made known un - to God. And the
-giv - ing let your re - quests be made known un - to God. And the
-giv - ing let your re - quests be made known un - to God. And the
Emi.t
p

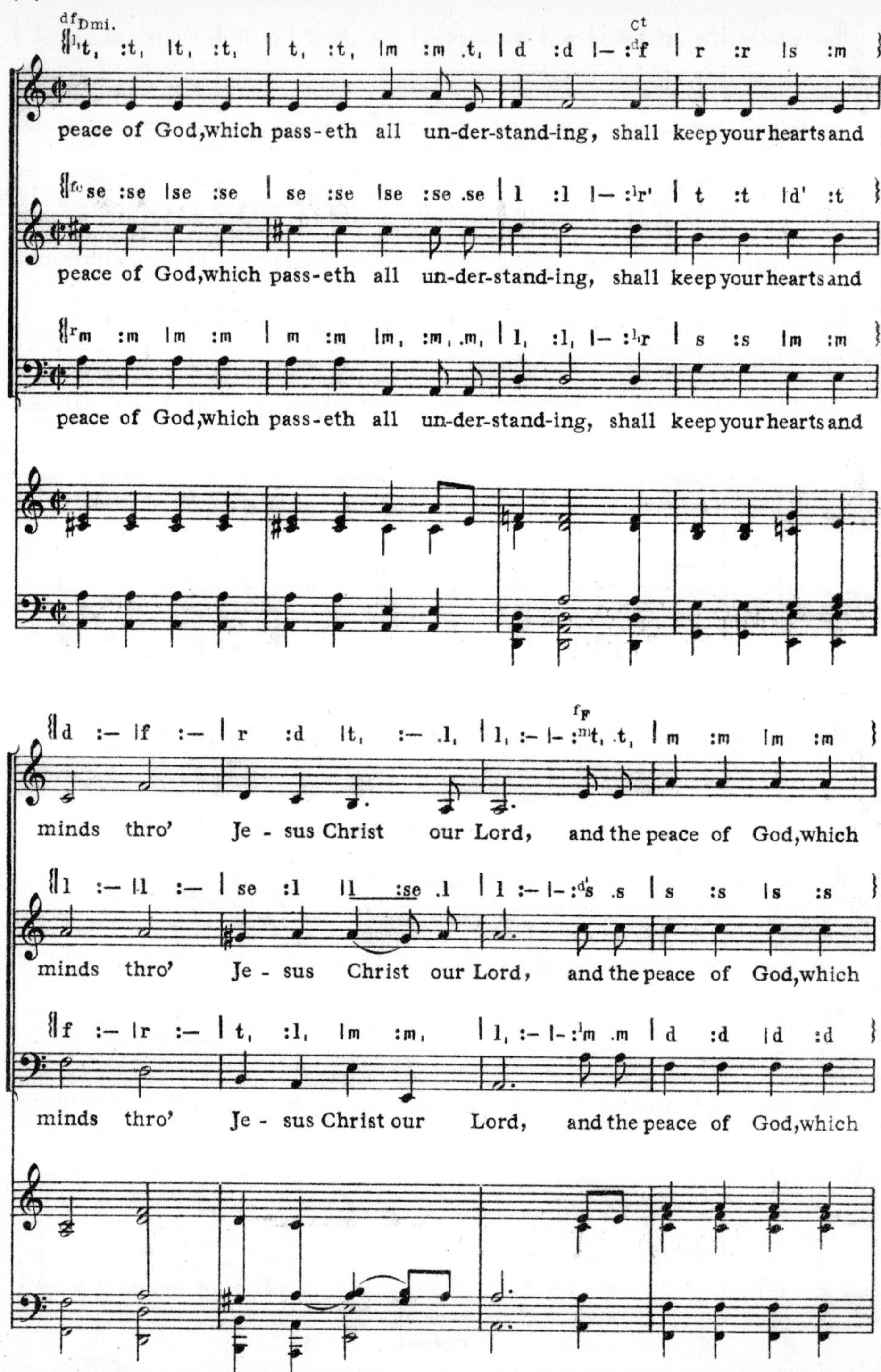
peace of God, which pass-eth all un-der-stand-ing, shall keep your hearts and
peace of God, which pass-eth all un-der-stand-ing, shall keep your hearts and
peace of God, which pass-eth all un-der-stand-ing, shall keep your hearts and
minds thro' Je - sus Christ our Lord, and the peace of God, which
minds thro' Je - sus Christ our Lord, and the peace of God, which
minds thro' Je - sus Christ our Lord, and the peace of God, which

poco
pass - eth all un-der- stand - ing, shall keep your hearts and minds through
pass - eth all un-der- stand - ing, shall keep your hearts and minds through
pass - eth all un-der- stand - ing, shall keep your hearts and minds through
rall.
pp
Je - sus Christ our Lord, through Je - sus Christ our Lord.
Je - sus Christ our Lord, through Je - sus Christ our Lord.
Je - sus Christ our Lord, through Je - sus Christ our Lord.
(sempre pp)

(pp)
: |s' :— |f' :m' |r' :d' | d' :— :d | s :—.f :m
Re - joice in the
: | : | : | : | : :d' | m' :—.r' :d'
Re - joice in the
: | : | : | : | : :d | d' :—.t :d'
Re - joice in the
(ppp)
f

|f :r :— |s :— :l .,m |f :— :r |m :d :— |t, :— :r
Lord al - way, and a-gain I say, re - joice. Re -
|r' :t :— |d' :— :m' .,m' |l :— :s |s :— .l :fe |s :— :t
Lord al - way, and a-gain I say, re-joice. Re -
|f :s :— |m :— :de .,de |r :— :t, |d :l, :— |s, :— :s
Lord al - way, and a-gain I say, re - joice. Re -
|s :-.f :m |l :f :— |r :— :s .,r |m :-.f :s |f :r :—
-joice in the Lord al - way, and a-gain I say, re -
|t :-.t :de' |r' :— :l .t,d' |t :— :r' .,r' |s :— :d' |r' :t :—
-joice in the Lord al - way, and a-gain I say, re -
|m :-.m :l |f :r :— |s :— :t, .,t, |d :-.r :m |f :s :—
-joice in the Lord al - way, and a-gain I say, re -

* The original Echo-Interlude of 12 bars may be inserted here. See Purcell Society's edition [Ed.]

Words by
WILLIAM ROMANIS
(1824-99)
Melody by ADAM DRESE
(1620-1701)
v. 1. Harm. S.S.WESLEY
v. 2. " HENRY G. LEY
v. 3. " J.S.BACH
Slowly
Key A
SOP.
ALTO
TEN.
BASS
1. Round me falls the night; Saviour, be my light
Thro' the hours in dark-ness shroud-ed Let me see Thy face un-cloud-ed;
Let Thy Glo-ry shine In this heart of mine.
2. Earth-ly work is done,
Earth-ly sounds are none; Rest in sleep and silence seeking, Let me hear Thee

This anthem may be sung unaccompanied.

Reprinted by permission of the Society for Promoting Christian Knowledge.

soft-ly speak-ing; In my spi-rit's ear Whis-per, 'I am near.'

8 quavers in a bar

(Harmonies by J. S. BACH)

3. Bles-sed heavenly Light Shin-ing thro' earth's night: Voice that oft of

Shin-ing thro' earth's night:

love hast told me; Arms so strong to clasp and hold me:

told me; to clasp and hold me:

hold me:

Thou Thy watch wilt keep, Sa-viour, o'er my sleep.

79 SUBDUE US BY THY GOODNESS

Words from the German

JOHANN SEBASTIAN BACH
(1685–1750)
Arranged and edited by
W. GILLIES WHITTAKER
(*Melody from Erfurt Enchiridion* 1524)

-due us by Thy good - ness.
A -
-wake us by Thy grace;

dim.
p
That men whose hearts are
wear - y,

May life a - new em -
brace.
And_
cresc.

mp
though earth's woes be near us,
mp
mp
cresc.
Thy
cresc.
cresc.
mf
Spi - rit still shall cheer us.
mf
mf

cresc.
All
cresc.
cresc.
praise and thanks to Thee!
f
f
f

80 THE DAY DRAWS ON WITH GOLDEN LIGHT

Aurora lucis rutilat
Tr. THOMAS ALEXANDER LACEY
(1853–1931)

EDWARD C. BAIRSTOW

From the Oxford Series of Easy Anthems, reprinted by permission.
Words reprinted by kind permission of the English Hymnal Committee.
Founded on an Angers Church Melody.

{|r :— :m |f :m :r |m :—:— |— : :d |s, :— :l, |ta, :— :s }

lifts an an - swering cheer, ——— The

{|d :— :r |m :d :f |m :— :r |d :— :— |— : : |la, :s, :ta, }

deep makes moan with wail - ing fear. ———

cresc.

{|l, :d :d |m :— :f |s :— :s |l :s :f }

SOP. & ALTO *f*

{|l, :d :d |m :r :d |t, :f :m |m :— :r }

For lo, ——— He comes, the might - y

{|l, :d :d |d' :t :l |m :r :d |f :— :l }

TEN. & BASS unis *f*

f

King, To take from death his pow'r and sting,
To tram - ple down his gloom-y reign, And break
And break the
the wea - ry pris - 'ner's chain.
wea - ry, wea - ry pris - 'ner's chain.
Ch.
Sw.

Ma-ker of
all, to Thee we pray, Ful - fil in us Thy
Ma-ker of all, to Thee we pray, Ful-fil in us Thy
p unis.
Ful - fil in us Thy
Ch.
Sw.
joy to - day.
When death as -
unis. p
cresc.
When death as - sails, grant
Ch. to Sw.
cresc.

cresc.
sails, grant, Lord, that we
Lord that we
p Ch.
dim.
Sw.
Ch.
May share Thy Pas-chal
May share, may share Thy Pas -
p unis.
May share Thy Pas-chal vic - to - ry, Thy
Sw.
vic - to - ry. A - men.
rit.
- chal vic - to - ry. A - - - men.
rit.
Pas - chal vic - to - ry. A - men. A - men.
Sw.
rit.

81 THE HEAVENS DECLARE THE CREATOR'S GLORY

From 'A STUDENT'S HYMNAL' (Hymns of the Kingdom) by the Oxford University Press.

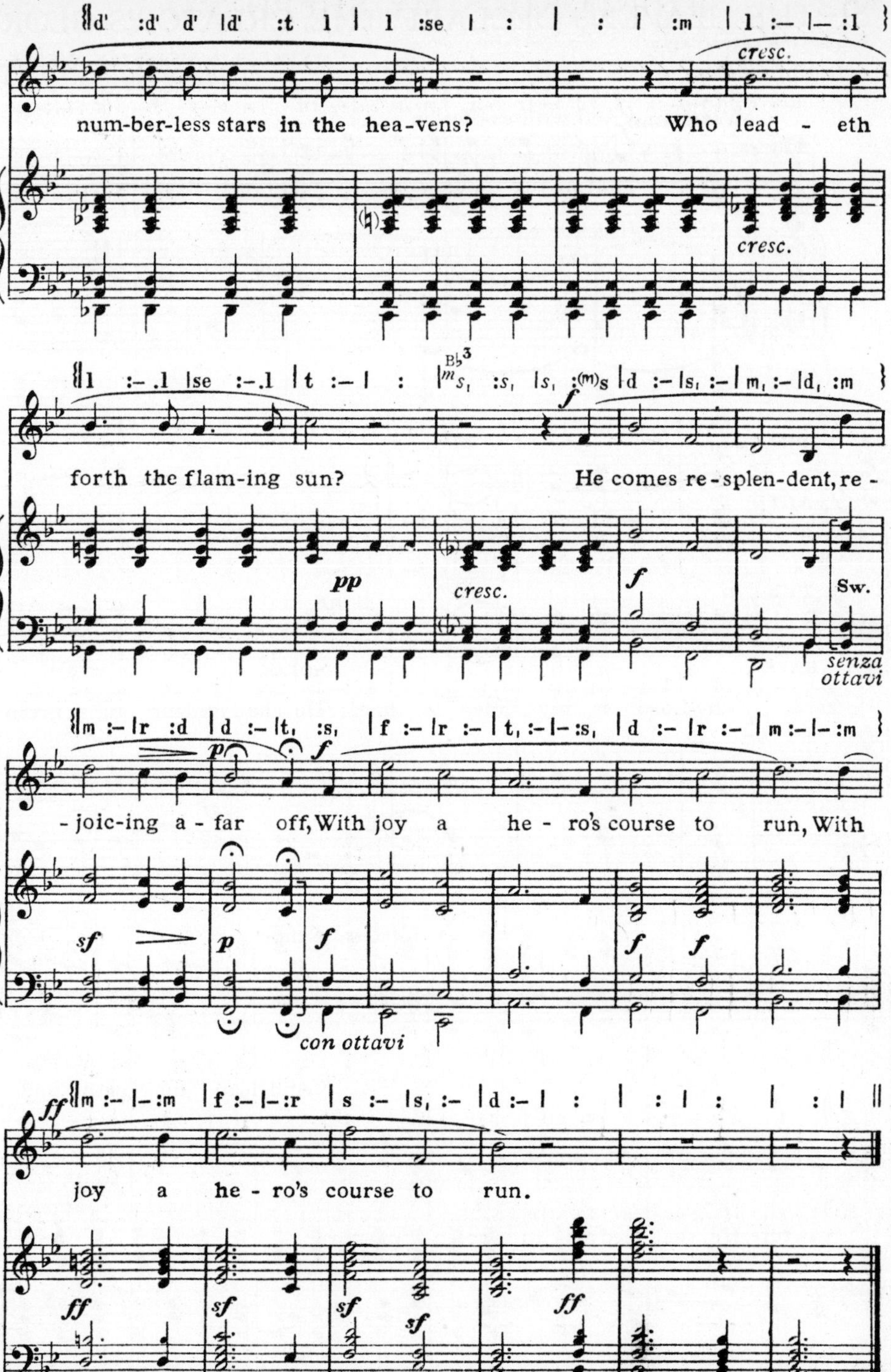
num-ber-less stars in the hea-vens? Who lead - eth
cresc.
forth the flam-ing sun? He comes re-splen-dent, re -
cresc.
Sw.
senza ottavi
-joic-ing a - far off, With joy a he - ro's course to run, With
con ottavi
joy a he - ro's course to run.

82 THE LORD IS MY SHEPHERD

Words from 23rd Psalm

SAMUEL SEBSASTIAN WESLEY (1810-76)

NOTE: The bracketed organ part [ ] may well be omitted. [Ed.]

[Org.]
lead me forth be - side the wa-ters of com - fort;
[Small notes refer to organ part]
He
He shall con - vert my soul, He
[Org.]
shall con-vert, con - vert my soul, and bring, and bring me
He shall my soul, and bring me
shall con - vert, con - vert my soul and bring me forth
He shall con - vert my soul and bring, and bring me
forth in the paths of righ- teous - ness, bring me
forth in the paths of righ- teous - ness, bring me
in - to the paths of righ - teous - ness, bring me
forth in the paths, the paths of righ - teous - ness, bring me

forth in the paths of righ - teous-ness, He shall con -
forth in the paths of righ - teous-ness, He shall
forth in the paths of righ - teous-ness, He shall con -
forth in the paths of righ - teous-ness, He
- vert, con - vert my soul; He shall con - vert, con -
con - vert my soul, con -
- vert my soul; He shall con - vert con -
shall con - vert, He shall con - vert, con -
vert my soul, and bring me forth, and bring me forth be -
- vert my soul, and bring me forth, bring me forth be -
- vert my soul, and bring me forth, and bring me forth be -
- vert my soul, and bring me forth be -
rall.
p
- side the wa-ters of com - fort for His name's sake.
rall.
p

♪=88

SOPRANO SOLO

‖ :*mf* m :m .m | l :d' .,d' | t .t :l .,l | se .se :l | m :m }

Yea, tho' I walk thro' the val-ley of the shadow of death, I —

p

‖ — :r | d :t, | l, :— | se, : | **BASS SOLO** *f* s, .s, :— | l, :t, }

— will fear no e - vil. For Thou art with

‖ d :— | m :— | m :— | f :r | s :— | — :— | s :m .,r | d :— ‖

ritard.

me, Thy rod and Thy staff com-fort — me.

Andante con moto (one in a bar)

Thy lov-ing kind-ness and mer-cy shall fol - low me all the

‖ m :r :d | d :t, :d | r :r :m | s :— :f | m : : | l :— :l }

SOP. *p* *mf*

ALTO

‖ s, :s, :s, | s, :s, :d | d :d :d | d :r :— | d :d :d | d :— :r }

Thy lov-ing kind-ness and mer-cy shall fol-low me all the days, the

Thy lov-ing kind-ness and mer-cy shall fol-low me all the

‖ s :f :m | m :r :s | l :l :d' | d' :s :— | s : : | l :— :t }

TEN. *p* *mf*

BASS ‖ d :t, :d | s, :f, :m, | f, :f, :s, | l, :t, :— | d : : | f :— :f }

This movement may be thought of as with one beat in a bar, not three. *[Ed.]*

days, the days of my life; And I will dwell, will dwell in the
days, the days of my life; And I will dwell, will dwell in the
days, the days of my life; And I will dwell, will dwell in the
house of the Lord, of the Lord for ev - er, will dwell for ev - er, for -
house, the house of the Lord for - ev - - -
house, the house of the Lord for - ev - er, for - ev - er, for
house of the Lord, of the Lord for - ev - er, for - ev - er, will
- ev - er, will dwell for - ev - er, for ev - er and
- er, will dwell for - ev - er, for ev - - -
- ev - er, will dwell for - ev - er, and I will dwell in the house,
dwell, dwell for - ev - er, and I will dwell in the house of the

ev - er, the house of the Lord for - ev - er, in the
- - er, the house of the Lord, will dwell in the house of the Lord,
the house of the Lord for - ev - er, in the
Lord, in the house of the Lord
house of the Lord, and I will dwell
of the Lord, will dwell for - ev - er, dwell
house of the Lord for - ev - er, I will dwell in the house,
for - - - ev - er, will dwell for - ev - - - - - - - - er
in the house of the Lord for - ev - - - er,
cresc.
for - ev - - - - er, for - ev - - - er,
in the house of the Lord, of the Lord for - ev - er,
cresc.
in the house of the Lord for - ev - - - er,
dim.
ritard. p
for - ev - - - - - - - er, for - ev - er.
dim.
ritard. p

83 THE SOULS OF THE RIGHTEOUS

from 'GOD CREATED MAN'

Wisdom iii, 1, 3.

H. WALFORD DAVIES

SOLO
touch ——— them, are in the hand of
SOPRANO
p
cresc.
The souls of the righteous are in the hand of
ALTO
p
cresc.
The souls of the right - eous are in the hand of
TENOR
p
cresc.
The souls of the right - eous are in the hand of
BASS
p
cresc.
The souls of the right - eous are in the hand of

molto cresc.
dim.
God, are in the hand of God, no torment shall
God, are in the hand of God, no torment shall
molto cresc.
dim.
God, the hand of God, no torment shall
God, the hand of God, no torment shall
molto cresc.
dim.
God, the hand of God, no torment shall

touch them, no tor - ment shall touch — them.
touch them, shall — touch them.
(SOLO)
(CHORUS)
touch them, no — tor - ment shall touch them.
(SOLO)
(CHORUS)
touch them, no — tor - ment shall touch them.
touch them, shall — touch them.

pp
They are in peace,
they are in peace.
They are in peace,
they are in peace.
They are in peace,
they are in peace.
They are in peace,
they are in peace.
They
They are in peace.
pp

84 THE STRIFE IS O'ER

From 'Six Short Anthems' Oxford University Press.

Hal - le - lu - jah, Hal - le - lu - jah.
Gt. & Sw.
Death's might-iest powers have done their worst, and Je - sus
reduce
hath His foes dis - persed; Let shouts of praise and

joy out - burst. Hal - le - lu - jah, Hal - le - lu - jah,
cresc.
mf Sw.
Hal-le-lu-jah!
On the third morn He
Gt. & Sw.
mf Sw.
rose a-gain, Glo-rious in ma - jes - ty to reign:

*This descant is optional, and the Trebles can sing in unison with the Altos if required.

cresc.
sting Thy ser - vants free, that we may live, and sing to
cresc.
ff
poco rit.
Thee, Hal - le - lu - jah, Hal - le - lu - jah, Hal - le - lu -
f Gt. & Sw.
poco rit.
senza rit.
ff
- jah!
A - men.
a tempo
ff
cresc.
ff

85

THEE WE ADORE

GIOVANNI PERLUIGI SANTE DA PALESTRINA
(1525–94)

This anthem to be sung unaccompanied.

-ly Name Thy ho - - ly Name; Who,
praise and bless Thy ho - - ly Name; Who, by Thy
-ly Name and praise and bless Thy ho - - - - - -
and praise and bless Thy ho - - ly Name;
by Thy pre - - cious cross most ho - - - -
pre - cious cross, Thy cross most ho - -
-ly Name; Who, by Thy pre-cious cross most ho - -
Who, by Thy pre - cious cross most ho - -

-ly, hast re - deem'd Thy peo -

-ly, hast re - deem'd Thy peo - ple, hast redeem'd Thy

-ly, hast re deem'd Thy peo - ple, hast re -

-ly, hast redeem'd Thy peo - ple,

- - ple, hast re - deem'd Thy peo - - - - -

peo - - ple, hast re - deem'd Thy peo - -

-deem'd Thy peo - ple, hast re - deem'd Thy peo - - - - -

hast re - deem'd Thy peo - - - - -

Bmi.t
-ple. Who by Thy pre - - - cious cross most ho -
-ple. Who by Thy pre - cious cross most ho -
-ple. Who by Thy pre-cious cross most ho -
-ple. Who by Thy pre - cious cross most
pp
rall.
- - ly hast re-deem'd Thy peo - ple.
- - ly hast re-deem'd Thy peo - ple.
- - ly hast redeem'd Thy peo - - ple.
ho - ly hast redeem'd Thy peo - ple.
fp
rall.

86 THEIR* BODIES ARE BURIED IN PEACE

Ecclesiasticus xliv. 15

GEORGE FREDERICK HANDEL
(1685–1759)

QUARTET
Grave e Piano

*The words 'His' or 'Her' with singular verb may on occasion be substituted.

bo - dies are bu - - ried in peace,
Their
in peace,
are bu - ried in peace,
bo - dies are bu - - ried in peace.
are bu - ried in peace.
in peace.

CHORUS
Andante moderato
SOP.
ALTO
TEN.
BASS
But their name liv - eth ev - er-more, but their name liv -
- eth ev - er - more, but their name liv - eth ev - er-more,
but their name liv - eth ev - er - more, their name their
Andante moderato

their name
mf
name
their name
mf
their name
liv - eth ev - er - more,
liv - eth ev - er - more,
liv - eth ev - er - more,
liveth
livethev - er - more,
their name
cresc.
their name, their name,
ev - er - more,
their name, their name,
cresc.
their name,
cresc.

But their name liv - eth ev - er-more,
but their name liv - eth ev - er - more, but their name liv - eth
Allargando
ev - er-more, but their name liv - eth ev - er - more.
Allargando

QUARTET
Grave e Piano
Key D♭
Their bo-dies are bu-ried in peace, in peace,
Grave e Piano
are bu - - - ried in peace, their bo-dies are
bu-ried in peace, are bu-ried in peace.

CHORUS

Andante moderato

their name
-more; their name
their name, their name
their name
liv - eth ev - er - more,
liv-eth ev - er - more,
liv-eth ev - er - more,
liv-eth ev - er - more,
their name, name,
their name,
cresc.

their name,
their name, their name, But their name liv-eth
their name
ev - er-more, but their name liv - eth ev - er - more, but their
allargando
name liv - eth ev - er more, but their name liv - eth ev - er - more.

87 THOU JUDGE OF QUICK AND DEAD

CHARLES WESLEY (1707–1788)

SAMUEL SEBASTIAN WESLEY (1810–76)

Lento (𝅗𝅥 = 56)

Key B mi

CHORUS

SOPRANO ALTO

Thou Judge of quick and dead, Before whose

TENOR BASS

Lento (𝅗𝅥 = 56)

bar se - vere, With ho - ly joy, or guil - ty dread, We

* This may either be quietly sung by contraltos or left to the tenors and basses. [*Ed.*]

CHORUS
all shall soon ap - pear; Do Thou our souls pre - pare
For that tre - men - dous day, pre - pare for that tre - men - dous
day; And fill us now with watch - ful care, And teach our
day; And fill us now with watch
day; And fill us now with watch - - ful care,

cresc.
dim.
hearts to pray, and teach, and teach our hearts to pray.
- - ful care, And teach our hearts to pray.
And teach, and teach our hearts to pray.
Andante sostenuto, sempre legato
CHORUS
Oh, may we thus in - sure A lot a - mong the
Andante sostenuto(♩ = 132)
Oh, may we thus in - sure A lot a-mong the
blest, thus in - sure,

p CHORUS
Oh, may we thus in - sure A lot a-mong the blest, the
CHORUS p
Oh,
blest, thus in - sure a lot a - mong the
in - sure A lot a - mong the blest,
blest,
And watch a moment, to se -
may we thus in - sure A lot a-mong the blest, a lot a-mong the
blest,
Oh, may we thus in - sure,
a lot a-mong the blest, the blest, a lot a-mong the

C♯ mi.t m l, :se, | :m | ba :se | l :d' | A t d' s :— | — :— | f :— | — :— | — :— | — :— | fD m :t

cresc.

-cure An ev-er-last-ing rest. Oh,

fe t, :— | : | : | : | : | :l m, | f, :s, | l, :d | d :t, | — :d s

cresc.

blest, And watch a moment, Oh,

:t m | ba :se | l :t | d' :m' | m' t :— | l :— | l :s | f :s.l | s :— | :d s

cresc.

And watch a mo-ment, to se - cure, to se - cure, And

t m :— | m :— | m :r | d :t,.l, | r l, :— | d :— | r :— | r, :— | s, :— | :l m

cresc.

blest, And watch a mo - ment to se - cure, And

cresc.

l :t | d' :t | m' :— | — :r' | d' :t | l :t.d' | F♯ mi. t m :— | — :— | — :m | m :—.m

f *dim.*

may we thus in-sure A lot a-mong the blest, And watch a

m :r | d :r | m :— | f :— | m :r | d :r.m | r s, :se, | l, :le, | t, :d | r :d .t,

f *dim.*

may we thus in-sure A lot a-mong the blest, And watch a mo-ment, to se-

s :— | — :— | — :— | l :t | d' :— | s :— | t m :— | — :— | — :ba | se :l .t

f *dim.*

watch a mo - ment, watch, and watch a

d :r | m :r | d :— | — :d | d :— | d :— | s d, :— | :s, | se, :l, | t, :d .r

f *dim.*

watch a mo - ment, to se - cure, a mo-ment, to se-

f *dim.*

dim.
p
mo-ment, to se - cure An ev - er - last - ing rest,
-cure, se - cure An ev - er - last - ing rest. Oh,
mo-ment, a mo-ment, to se-cure an ev - er - last - ing rest, Oh,
-cure An ev - er - last - ing rest,
And
may we thus in - sure A lot a-mong the blest, And watch a
may we thus in - sure A lot a-mong the blest, And watch a mo - ment
And watch a

watch_ a_ mo-ment, to se-cure_ An_ ev - er - last - ing
mo-ment, An ev-er - last - ing
a mo-ment, to se - cure
mo - ment, to_ se - cure An ev-er - last - - ing
rest, And watch_ a_ mo-ment, a_ moment, to se-cure an
rest, And watch a mo-ment, a mo - ment, to se-
rest, An ev - er - last - - ing rest,
legato
rest, And watch_ a mo - ment, to se-cure, and watch a

ev - er - last - - - ing rest, an ev - er -
legato
-cure An ev-er - last - - - ing rest, an ev - er-
an ev - er -
mo-ment, to se-cure An ev-er - last - - - - ing rest,
dim.
p legato
-last - ing rest, an ev-er - last - ing rest, And watch a mo-ment to se-
dim.
p
-last - - - ing rest, an ev - -
dim.
p
-last - ing, ev - er - last - ing rest, ev-er- last - -
p
an ev-er, ev - er-last - ing rest,
dim.
p

-cure An ev - er - last -
- er - last - - - ing rest, an
- ing rest, an ev - er - last - ing rest, an
an ev - er, ev - er -
p rit.
- - ing rest, ev - er - last - ing rest!
ev - er - last - ing rest, ev - er - last - ing rest!
ev - er - last - ing rest, ev - er - last - ing rest!
-last - - ing rest, ev - er - last - ing rest!
(soft Solo Stop)
rit.

88 THOU KNOWEST, LORD

From the Burial Service

HENRY PURCELL (1658–95)

Lento ma non troppo

NOTE: This anthem may well be preceded by 'Man that is born of a woman' No. 57
To be sung unaccompanied.

dim.
mp
mer-ci-ful— Sa - viour, Thou most wor-thy Judge e - ter - nal,
p
cresc.
suf - fer us not, suf - fer us not, at our
dim.
p
last hour, for a - ny pains of death, for a - ny
for a - ny pains, for
Ped.
for a - ny pains of
dim. e rall.
pp
pains of death, to fall, to fall from Thee. A - men.
a - ny pains of death,
death, — to fall,

89 THOU, LORD, OUR REFUGE

Psalm xc. 1-2.

FELIX MENDELSSOHN-BARTHOLDY (1809-77)

Andante
Key D mi.
SOPRANO
ALTO
TEN.
BASS
Thou, Lord, our re - fuge hast been from age to age,
Ere Thou hadst brought
Ere Thou hadst brought forth, brought forth the
Ere Thou hadst brought forth,
Ere Thou hadst brought forth the
G mi.
cre
forth, Thou hadst brought forth the
moun - - - tains, Ere Thou hadst brought
Ere Thou hadst brought forth,
Ere Thou hadst brought

This anthem, originally written for 8 voices, may be sung unaccompanied. Small notes in brackets are only to be played in the organ part, when the organ accompanies the voices.

- scen - - - - - do
mountains, or the earth hadst form - ed,
forth the mountains, or the earth hadst form-ed,
- scen - - - - do
f
or the world cre - a - - - ted, Thou art
or the world cre - a - ted, Thou art
pp
God from ev - er - last - ing, world with - out
God from ev - er - last - - - - ing.
God from ev - er - last - ing, world with - out
end. Ere Thou hadst the
cresc.
p
Ere Thou hadst brought forth the moun-tains, or the
end. Ere Thou hadst brought forth the
cresc.

moun - tains, or the world cre - a - - -
earth, the earth
mountains, or the earth, or world cre - a - - - -
-ted, Thou art God from ev - er -
-last - ing, world with - out end. Hal - le -
Hal - le - lu - - - - - - jah.
-lu - jah,
Hal - le - lu - jah.
Hal - le - lu - - - - - - jah.

90 THOU VISITEST THE EARTH

Anthem for a Tenor Voice with Chorus

PSALM lxv

MAURICE GREENE
(1695-1755)

NOTE: The Solo may be sung by a Baritone or a Mezzo Soprano. [*Ed.*]

bless-est it, and crown - est the year, the year with Thy good-ness, and
crown-est the — year. the year with Thy good-ness; Thou crown - est the
year, the year with Thy good-ness; Thou crown-est the — year, the
CHORUS
Thou vi-sit-est the earth, and bless-est it: and
Thou vi-sit-est the — earth, and
Thou vi - sit-est the earth, and
CHORUS
year with Thy goodness. Thou vi-sit-est the earth, and

blessest it: and crown - - est the year with Thy good-ness. Thou
blessest it. and crownest the year, the year with Thy good-ness. Thou
blessest it: and crownest the year with Thy good-ness.
blessest it: and crownest the year with Thy good-ness Thy good-ness. Thou
crown-est the year, the year with Thy good-ness. Thou
crown - est the year with Thy good-ness.
Thou crown-est the year with Thy good-ness. Thou vi-sit-est the
crown - - est the year with Thy good-ness.
vi-sit-est the earth, and bless-est, and bless-est it, Thou crown-est the
cresc.
Thou vi-sit-est the earth, and bless-est it, Thou crown -
earth, Thou vi - sit-est the earth, and bless-est it,
cresc.
Thou vi-sit-est the earth, and bless-est it, Thou crown-est the

year the year with Thy good-ness, crown - - - est the
- est the year with Thy good-ness, Thou crown-est the year, the
Thou crown est the year, Thou crown-est the
year the year with Thy good-ness, Thou crown - - est the
year with Thy good-ness, Thou crown-est the year, the year with Thy
p
year with Thy good-ness, Thou crown - - est the year with Thy
year with Thy good-ness, Thou crown-est the
p
year with Thy good-ness, Thou crown-est the year, the year with Thy
good-ness, Thou crown - - est the year with Thy good-ness.
rall.
good-ness, Thou crown-est the year, the year with Thy good-ness.
year, Thou crown-est the year with Thy good-ness.
rall.
good-ness, Thou crown - - est the year with Thy good-ness.
rall.

91 THOU WILT KEEP HIM IN PERFECT PEACE

Isaiah xxvi. 3; Ps. cxxxix. 11; 1 John i. 5; Ps. cxix. 175.

SAMUEL SEBASTIAN WESLEY (1810–76)

R.

The dark-ness and the light to
but the night is as clear as the day.
to Thee are
Thee, to Thee are both a - like, to Thee are
to Thee are

Tempo I.
God is light, and in Him is no
both a - like. God is light, and
both a - like. God is light, and in
both a - like. God is light,
Tempo I.
senza Ped
dim.
dark - ness, in Him is no dark-ness at all.
in Him is no dark - ness at all.
in Him is no dark - - - ness at all. O let my
Him is no dark - - - ness at all. O
and in Him is no dark - ness at all.

cresc.
O let my soul live, and it shall praise
cresc.
cres.
O let my soul live, it shall praise
soul live, and it shall praise
cresc.
let my soul live, and it shall praise Thee, shall praise
let my soul live, and it shall praise
cresc.
Un poco accelerato (♩=80)
Thee,
mf
Thee, for Thine, Thine is the king - dom, the pow - er, and the
mf
Thee, for Thine is the king - dom, the power, and the
mf
Thee, for Thine is the
Un poco accelerato (♩=80)
mf [Op. Diap. Gt. Org.]
Ped. 16 ft.

for Thine is the king-dom, the pow-er, and the
cresc.
glo - ry, for ev - - - - - - - - - - -
glo - - - - - - - - - - - -
cresc.
glo - ry for ev - - - - - - - - -
cresc.
king-dom, the pow-er, and the glo - - - - - - -
cresc.
Tempo I.
dim.
glo - ry, for ev - - er more.
dim.
- - - - - - - - er - more.
- - - - - - - ry, for ev - er - more.
dim.
- - - er - more, ev - - er - more.
dim.
- - ry, for ev - - - - er - more.
Tempo I.
dim.
pp

Thou wilt keep him in per - fect peace, whose mind is stay -
Thou wilt keep him in per - fect peace,
Thou wilt keep him in per - - - - fect peace, whose
Thou wilt keep him in per - fect peace, whose mind is
Thou wilt keep him in per - fect peace, whose
senza Ped
dim.
p e sostenuto
ritard.
- ed on Thee, on Thee, is stay - ed on Thee.
whose mind is stay - ed on Thee, is stay - ed on Thee.
mind is stay - ed on Thee, is stay - - ed on Thee.
stay - - ed on Thee, is stay - - ed on Thee.
mind is stay - ed on Thee, is stay - - ed on Thee.
pp e sostenuto
Ped.

92 TURN THEE AGAIN, O LORD

Psalm xc. 13

THOMAS ATTWOOD
(1765–1838)

SEMI CHORUS

Key F ‖m :m :– .f | r :– :r | s :–.f :m .r | d :– :– | f :f :– ‖
p SOP

ALTO
‖d :d :– .d | l, :– :l, | s, :— :s, .f, | m,:– :– | d :d : ‖
Turn Thee a - gain, O Lord,— at the last, turn Thee,
‖s :s :– .l | f :– :f | r :— :t, .t, | d :– :– | l :l :– ‖
TEN.
p

BASS
‖d :d :– .d | d :– :d | t, :— :s, .s, | l,:– :– | : : ‖
Turn Thee a - gain, O Lord, at the last,

turn Thee, O Lord at— the last,— and be
‖m :m :de | r :– .r :m .f | d :t, :r .r ‖

‖t, :t, :ta, | l, :l, :— .l, | s, :— :— ‖
turn Thee, O Lord at the last.
turn Thee, O Lord at the last,— and be
‖se :se :m | f :f :— .f | m :r :t .t ‖

(Organ)
‖ : :s, | f, :f, :r, | s, :— :s .s ‖
O Lord at the last, and be

gra - cious, be gra - cious un - to Thy ser - vants, un - to Thy
‖r :r :r | s :s .s :l .s | s .f :f .f :s .f ‖

‖ : :r | r :d :d | d :t, :— ‖
be gra - cious un - to Thy
gra - cious un - to Thy ser - - - - - -
‖l :l .l :t .l | s :— :— | — :— :r ‖

‖f :f :f | m :— :m | r :— :s, ‖
gra - cious un - to Thy ser - - -

This anthem may be sung unaccompanied. Small notes refer to the organ part, when used.

ser-vants, be gra-cious, be gra-cious un - to Thy ser - vants.
ser - - vants, Thy ser - - vants.
vants, be gra-cious, be gra-cious un - to Thy ser - vants.
- vants, be gra-cious, be gra-cious un - to Thy ser - vants.
VERSE
Turn Thee a - gain, O Lord, at the last,
Turn Thee a - gain, O Lord, at the last, turn Thee,
Turn Thee a - gain, O Lord at the last,
turn Thee, turn Thee, turn Thee, turn Thee,
turn Thee, turn Thee, turn Thee, turn Thee,
turn Thee, turn Thee, turn, turn Thee, turn Thee,
turn Thee, turn Thee, turn Thee, turn Thee,
turn Thee a - gain, O Lord, at the last, and be
O Lord, at the last,

gra-cious, be gra-cious un-to Thy ser - vants, be
gra-cious un - to Thy ser - - vants, be
un - to Thy ser - - vants, be
Ped.

gra-cious, be gra-cious un-to Thy ser - - vants.
gra-cious un - to Thy ser - - vants.

CHORUS

pp
Turn Thee a-gain, O Lord, at the last, turn Thee,
pp
Turn Thee a-gain, O Lord, at the last,

turn Thee, O Lord, at the last, and be gra-cious, be
turn Thee, O Lord, at the last, be
turn Thee, O Lord, at the last, and be gra-cious un-to Thy
O Lord, at the last, and be gra-cious un -

gra - cious un - to ser - vants, un - to Thy ser - vants, be
gra - cious un - to Thy ser -
ser - - - - - vants, be
- to Thy ser - - vants, be
gra - cious, be gra - cious un - to Thy ser - -
- - - - vants, Thy ser - - -
gra - cious, be gra - cious un - to Thy ser - -
A - men,
- vants. A - - - men, A - -
SOP. II.
SOP. I.
SOP. II. mf
- vants. A - men, A - men, A - men,
Ped.
- vants. A - - - men, A -
A - men,
- - - men, A - - men, A - men.
SOP. I.
pp
A - men, A - men, A - men, A - men.
A - men, A - - - men, A - men.
- - men, A - men, A - men, A - men.

TURN THEE UNTO ME

turn Thee un-to me, O
Turn Thee un-to me, O Lord, O
un - to me,
O Lord, O
Thee un-to me, O Lord,
Lord,
f Ami.
O
Lord,
O Lord, O
Lord, O Lord, turn Thee un-to me, O
turn Thee un-to
Ped.

Emi.t
Lord, O Lord, O
turn Thee un-to me, O Lord,
Lord, turn Thee un-to me, O
Lord, O Lord, turn
me, O Lord,
cresc.
Lord, turn Thee un-to me, O
turn Thee un-to me, turn Thee un-to
Lord, O Lord, turn
Thee un-to me, O Lord, O Lord,
turn Thee un-to me, O Lord, turn
Ped.

Bmi.
Lord, O Lord,
me, O Lord, O
Thee un-to me, O Lord, O Lord, O
cresc.
O Lord, O
Thee un-to me, O
mf
O Lord,
Ami.
smoothly
Lord, and have mer - cy up-
Lord, O Lord, and have mer - cy up-
Lord, and have mer - cy up-
Lord, O Lord, and have mer - cy up-
Lord, O Lord, and have mer - cy up-

-on me, have mer - cy up - on me, have
-on me, have mer - cy up - on me, have
-on me, have mer - cy up - on me, have
-on me, have mer - cy up - on me, have
-on me, have mer - cy up - on me, have
mer - cy up - on me;
mer - cy up - on me;
mer - cy up - on me; for I am des - o -
mer - cy up - on me;
mer - cy up - on me; for
mp

Bmi.
mp
for I am des - o -
-late and in mis - er - y, I am
mp
for
I am des - o - late,
Emi.
-late and in mis - er -
des - o - late and in mis - er - y,
I am des - o - late and in
for
Ped.

cresc.
-y, I am
cresc.
for I am des - o-
cresc.
I am des - o - late, am des - o -
cresc.
mis - er - y, am des - o - late and
cresc.
I am des - o - late,
cresc.
des - o - late and in mis - er - y,
-late and in mis - er -
-late and in mis - er - y, am
mf sempre cresc.
in mis - er - y, for
mf sempre cresc.
for
mf sempre cresc.
Ped.

Emi.t
mf sempre cresc.
for I am des-o-late,
mf sempre cresc.
-y, am des-o-late and in
mf sempre cresc.
des-o-late, for I am des - o-
I am des-o-late and in miser-
I am des - o-late, for
dim.
for I am des - o-
dim.
mis - er - y, I
-late, I am des-o-late
dim.
-y, I am des - o - late, am
dim.
I am des - o - late and in
dim.

-late and in mis - - er -
— am des - o - late and in mis - er-
dim.
and in mis - er - y,
des - o - late and in mis - - er -
mis - - er - - y, in mis - er-
E maj.3
f subito
dim. e rall.
p
-y, am des - o - late and in mis - er-y.
-y, am des - o - late and in mis - er-y.
am des - o - late and in mis - er-y.
-y, am des - o - late and in mis - er-y.
-y, am des - o - late and in mis - er-y.

Lento tranquillo
SOPRANO DUET
The sor-rows of my heart are en - larg - ed; O
bring Thou me out of my trou - bles,
The
O bring Thou me, O
sor-rows of my heart are en - larg - ed; O bring Thou

— bring Thou me out — of — my — trou-bles.
me, O — bring Thou me — out of — my trou-bles.
The sor-rows of my heart are en - larg - ed;
O
O bring Thou me out of — my trou-bles.
— bring Thou me out — of — my trou-bles. Look

mf
Look — up - on — my ad-
— up - on — my ad - ver - si - ty,
-ver - si - ty, and for - give me all my
and for - give me all my sin, and for-
sin, all my sin, for - give me all my
-give me all my sin, and for - give me all my
rall. al fine
rall. al fine
rall. al fine

poco rit.
sin, for - give me all my sin.
sin, for - give me all my sin.
Andante con moto
CHORUS
SOP. I
O keep my soul, and de - liv - er me; for
SOP. II
O keep my soul, and de - liv - er me;
ALTO
O keep my soul, and de - liv - er me;
TEN.
O keep my soul, and de - liv - er me; let me
BASS
O keep my soul, and de - liv - er me;
Andante con moto

I have put my trust in Thee,
I have put my trust in
not be con-found - - - - ed,
let me
Ped.
let me
I have put my trust in
Thee, have put my trust in Thee, my
for
not be con-found - - - ed, for

not be con-found - - - - ed, for
Thee, in Thee, for
trust in Thee, let me
I have put my trust in Thee,
I have put my trust in Thee,
I have put my trust in Thee,
I have put my trust in Thee, let me
not be con-found - - - - ed,
let me not be con-
Man.

cresc.
let me not be confound - -
not be con-founded, let me not be con-
cresc.
let me not be con-founded, for I have
cresc.
-found-ed, let me not be con-found - ed, for I have
cresc.
cresc.
for I have put
cresc.
Ped.
-ed. O keep my
-found - - - - -ed. O keep my
put my trust in Thee. O keep my
put my trust in Thee. O keep my
my trust in Thee. O keep my

soul, and de - liv - er me; let me
soul, and de - liv - er me;
soul, and de - liv - er me; for
soul, and de - liv - er me;
soul, and de - liv - er me;
not be con - found - - - -
for I have put my
I have put my trust in Thee,
let me not be con - found -
let me
Ped.

- - ed, let me
trust in Thee, my trust in Thee, let me
my trust in Thee, let me
- - - - ed, let me
not be con-found - - - - -
not be con-found-ed, for I have put my
not be con-found-ed, for
not be con-found-ed, for I have put my
not be con-found-ed, for I have put my
ed.
cresc.

trust, have put my trust in Thee, have put
I have put my trust in Thee,
trust in Thee, let me not be con -
trust in Thee, in Thee,
my trust in Thee,
let me not be con -
- found - - - - -
for I have put my trust in
let me not be con - found - - -
Ped.

rall. al fine. ff
have put my trust, for
ff rall. al fine.
- found - - - ed, for I have
ff rall. al fine.
- ed, for I have put my trust in
ff rall. al fine.
Thee, for I have
ff rall. al fine.
- ed, for I have
ff rall. al fine.
Ped.
I have put my trust in Thee.
put my trust in Thee, my trust in Thee.
Thee, have put my trust in Thee.
put my trust, my trust in Thee.
put my trust, my trust in Thee.

94 TURN THY FACE FROM MY SINS

Psalm li. 9, 10, 11

THOMAS ATTWOOD (1765–1838)

SOP.
ALTO
pp
Turn Thy face from my sins, ___ and put out all my mis-
TEN.
BASS
-deeds.___ Make me a clean heart, O God,___ and re-
re - new, re - new,
-new a right_ spi - rit with - in me, re - new,
re - new, re -
re - new, re - new a right spi - rit with - in___
-new, re - new a right spi - rit, a right spi - rit with - in

||d :— |d :— |d :d |r :m |s :f |m :r |d :— |m :r |d :— | : ||

||l :— |l :— |s :s |s :d |l :— |l :l |s :— |f :— |m :— | : ||

me, re - new a right spi - rit with - in ______ me.

||f :— |d :— |d :d |d :— |r :— |r :r |m :— |t :— |d :— | : ||

||f :— |f :— |m :m |m :— |r :— |f :f |s :— |— :— |d :— | : ||

SOLO

||s :— |s :— |s :— |f :— |f :— |m :— |— :— |r :— |d :— |r :— |l :— |f :— |l :— |— :— |s :— |s :— }

mf

Cast me not a - way, ___ a - way from Thy pre - sence, and *p*

(*mp*)

||s :— |f :m |r :— |r :— |s :— |f :m |m :— |r :s |d' :— |r' :d' |t :— |d' :— }

take not Thy Ho - ly Spi - rit from me, and take not Thy Ho - ly

sempre legato

||l :— |t :l |l :— |s :d' |r :— |m :— |s :f |m :r |m :— |r :— |d :— |— :— ||

dim.

Spi - rit _ from me, Thy Ho - ly Spi - rit _ from me.

dim.

S

SEMI CHORUS
mf
Cast me not a - way, a - way from Thy pre -
-sence, and take not Thy Ho - ly Spi - rit from me, and take not Thy
dim.
Ho - ly Spi - rit from me, Thy Ho - ly Spi - rit from me.
dim.
poco rit.

95 WASH ME THROUGHLY FROM MY WICKEDNESS

Psalm li. 2, 3

SAMUEL SEBASTIAN WESLEY (1810-76)

f D mi.
all my sin, wash me throughly from my wickedness, and for -
- give me all my sin, and for - give, for-give, for-
all my sin, wash me throughly and for-give, for-
all my sin, all my sin, and for-give me
Ped.
f B♭
D mi.
- give me all my sin, all, all my sin.
- give me all my sin, all my sin, all my sin.
- give me all my sin, and for - give me all, all, all my sin.
all my sin, and for - give me all my sin.

For I ac - know - ledge my
cresc.
dim.
For I ac - know - ledge my faults, and my
faults, and my sin is ev-er be-fore me, my sin,

For I ac - know - ledge my faults, and my sin is
sin is ev - er be - fore me, my sin is
for I ac - know - ledge my faults, and my
For I ac - know - ledge my faults,
ev - er be - fore me, for I ac -
ev - er be - fore me,
sin, my sin, I ac - know - ledge my faults, and my

I ac-know-ledge my faults.
dim.
-know - - - ledge my faults.
I— ac-know - ledge my faults.— Wash me through-ly
sin is ev - er be-fore me.
Wash me
from my wicked-ness, and for-give me all my sin,—
mf

through-ly from my wickedness, and for-give me all my
for I ac-know - ledge my faults, my faults, my
for I ac-know - - ledge my faults, ac-know-ledge my
wash
cresc.
mf
sin,
faults, wash me through-ly from my wicked-ness, and for-
faults wash me, and for-
me, wash me, and for-
and for-
Gmi.
D maj.
p

cresc.
p
-give me all my sin, and for - give me all
-give me all my sin, and for - give me all
-give me all my sin, and for - give me all
-give me all my sin, and for - give me all
dim. e rall.
pp
my sin, and for - give me all my sin.
my sin, and for - give me all my sin.
my sin, and for - give me all my sin.
my sin, and for - give me all my sin.

96 WE LOVE THE PLACE

Words adapted from Psalm lxxxiv by the Rt. Rev. the Bishop of Oxford and Steuart Wilson

JOHANNES BRAHMS (1833-97)
Arranged for organ by CHARLTON PALMER

From 'Brahms' Requiem' (O.U.P. edition)

Lord of hosts, where Thine hon - our
Lord of hosts, where Thine hon - our
Lord of hosts, where Thine hon - our
Lord of hosts, where Thine hon - our
Fl.
Cor.
Str. & Wind
dwells, O Lord of hosts.
dwells, O Lord of hosts.
dwells, O Lord of hosts.
dwells, O Lord of hosts, O Lord of hosts.
Vln.
Viola & Clar.

p espress.
We love the place where Thine
hon - our dwells, O Lord of hosts.
p espress.
We love

p espress.
We love the place where Thine
p espress.
We love the place where Thine
We love the place
the place where Thine
hon - our dwells, O Lord of hosts.
hon - our dwells, O Lord of hosts.
where Thine hon - our dwells, O Lord of hosts.
hon - our dwells, O Lord of hosts.
Str.
p
Cello pizz.

Yea, my soul
Yea, my soul
Yea, my soul
Yea, my soul
It
Wind
it
cresc.
it long - eth, yea
it long-eth, yea faint-eth, it long- - -
long - eth, yea faint-eth, it long-eth, yea faint-eth, it long - -
Str.
Cor.
Wind
cresc.

long-eth, yea fainteth, yea faint - eth for Thy
faint-eth, it longeth yea faint - eth for Thy
-eth, yea faint - - - eth for Thy
-eth, yea faint-eth, faint - eth for Thy
Wind
Str. & Wind
pizz.
courts, my King and my God.
courts, my King and my God.
courts, my King and my God.
courts, my King and my God.

4 Gmi.
My heart and flesh cry out for God,
My heart and flesh cry out for God,
My heart and flesh cry out for God,
My heart and flesh cry out for God,
Str. fp
fp
fp
fp
Str. & Wind
4 Gb
Yea, for the liv - - - ing God,
Yea, for the liv - ing God, My heart and
Yea, for the liv - ing God, My heart and
Yea, for the liv - ing God, My heart and
mf
fp
Str.

cresc.
cri - eth out,
flesh cri - eth out, Yea, for the liv - ing,
flesh cri - eth out, Yea, for the liv -
flesh cri - eth out, Yea, for the
fp
cresc.
Str. & Wind
Yea, for the liv - ing God.
yea, for the liv - ing God.
- ing, yea, for the liv - ing God.
liv - ing, yea, for the liv - ing God.
f
Str.
L.H.

We
We
We
We
Wind
Cor.
Str. & Wind
love the place where Thine hon - our dwells, O Lord
love the place where Thine hon - our dwells, O Lord
love the place where Thine hon - our dwells, O Lord
love it where Thine hon - our dwells, O

of hosts, O Lord of hosts,
of hosts, O Lord of hosts,
of hosts, O Lord of hosts,
Lord of hosts, O Lord of hosts,
where Thine hon - our dwells, O Lord
where Thine hon - our dwells, O Lord
where Thine hon - our dwells, O Lord
where Thine hon - our dwells, O Lord of
Str. & Wind

of hosts.
of hosts.
of hosts.
hosts, O Lord of hosts.
Vla.&
Clt.
p
Blest are they,
Blest are they,
Blest are they,
Blest are they,

How blest, how blest are
How blest, how blest are
How blest, how blest are
How blest, how blest are
cresc.
they that dwell in Thy house They sing Thy
they that dwell in Thy house!
they that dwell in Thy house!
they that dwell in Thy house! They sing Thy

praise ev - er - more,
They sing Thy praise ev - er - more, ev - er - more, ev - er,
They sing Thy praise ev - er - more, sing Thy praise, sing Thy
praise ev - er - more,
They sing Thy praise, they
They sing Thy praise,
they sing Thy
ev - er - more, ev - er - more, they sing Thy praise ev - er - more,
praise ev - er - more, they sing Thy praise ev - er - more,
sing Thy praise ev - er - more,
they sing Thy

praise ev - er - more, ev - er - more,
they
they sing Thy praise ev - er -
praise ev - er - more, ev - er - more, they sing Thy_ praise ev - er -
f Fmi.
E♭t
they sing, __ they sing
sing Thy praise ev - er - more, they sing ___ Thy praise, __
-more, they sing Thy praise ev - er - more, they sing, __ sing Thy praise,
-more, they

— Thy praise, they — sing Thy praise for
they sing Thy — praise ev - er,
theysing — Thy praise, Thy praise for
sing — Thy praise, Thy praise, — they sing Thy praise
p dimin.
ev - - er - - more. We
p dolce
ev - - er - - more.
ev - - er - - more. We
ev - - er - - more.
Vln. pizz.
p
Wind. p
Cor.

love the place of Thine hon - our,
p dolce
We love the place of Thine
love the place of Thine hon - our,
p dolce
We love the place of Thine
Str.
Wind
Str.
Cor.
Vla.
p
cresc.
We love the
hon - our, Thine hon - our, We love the place, We
We love the
hon - our, Thine hon - our, We love the place, We
Str. & Wind.
cresc.

place O Lord of
love the place, the place where Thine hon - our dwells, O Lord of
place O Lord of
love the place, the place where Thine hon - our dwells, O Lord of
dim.
hosts.
hosts.
hosts.
hosts.
Wind

97 WHEN JESUS OUR LORD

Matt ii. 1,2; Numb. xxiv. 17; Ps. ii. 9.
From the unfinished Oratorio 'Christus'

FELIX MENDELSSOHN-BARTHOLDY
(1809–47)

Andante
TEN. SOLO
Say, where is He born, the King of Ju-
BASS I SOLO
BASS II SOLO
Andante
for we have seen, have seen His
-dae - a? for we have seen His star, we have seen His
for we have seen have seen His
sempre staccato
cresc.
star, have seen His star, and are come to a-dore Him, have seen His
cresc.
cresc.
have seen His
cresc.

star, and are come to a - dore Him, are
come to a - dore Him. Say, where is
He_born, the King of Ju - dae - a? for we have seen, have seen His

(This anthem may well be followed by the Chorus which succeeds it in *Christus*, 'There shall a star.' *Ed.*)

98 WHEN TO THE TEMPLE MARY WENT

*Translated from the German by
THE REV. J. TROUTBECK

JOHANN ECCARD
(1533 - 1611)

*The words are reprinted by kind permission of Novello & Co. Ltd.
This anthem to be sung unaccompanied

brought the Ho - ly Child, Him
And brought the Ho - ly Child, Him did the
went, And brought the Ho - ly Child, Him did the
And brought the Ho - ly Child, Him
went, And brought the Ho - ly Child, Him did the
brought the Ho - ly Child, Him did the
mf

did the a - ged Sim - eon see, As it had been re - veal'd.
a - ged Sim - eon see, As it had been re -
a - ged Sim - - eon see, As it had been re -
did the a - ged Sim - eon see, As it had been re -
a - ged Sim - - eon see, As it had been re -
a - ged Sim - eon see, As it had been re -

He took up Je - sus in his arms, and bless-ing God, he
-veal'd. He took up Je - sus in his arms, and bless-ing God, he
-veal'd. He took up Je - sus in his arms, and bless-ing God, he
-veal'd. He took up Je - sus in his arms, and bless-ing God, he
-veal'd. He took up Je - sus in his arms, and bless-ing God, he
-veal'd. He took up Je - sus in his arms, and bless-ing God, he

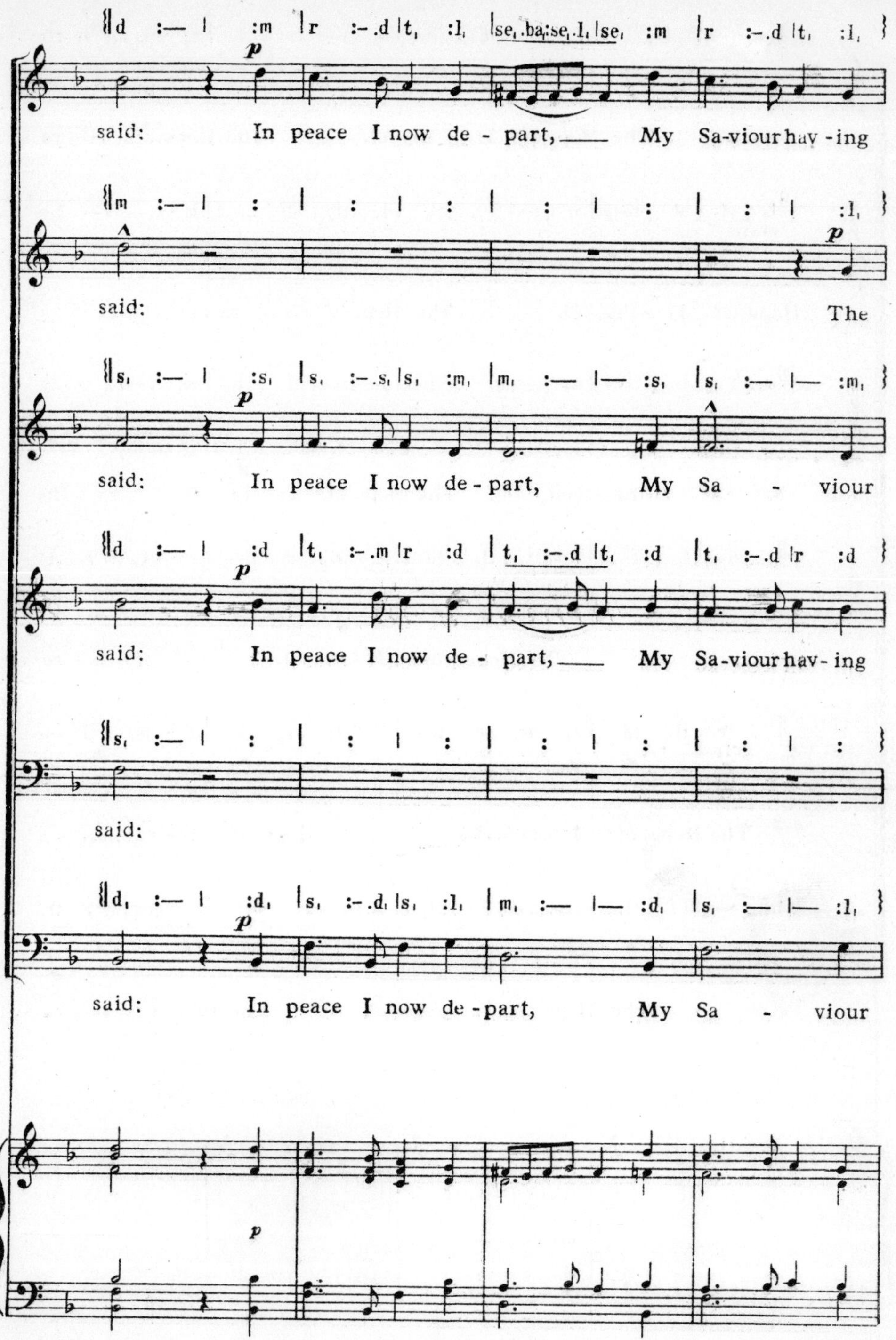
said: In peace I now de - part, My Sa-viour hav - ing
said: The
said: In peace I now de - part, My Sa - viour
said: In peace I now de - part, My Sa-viour hav - ing
said:
said: In peace I now de - part, My Sa - viour

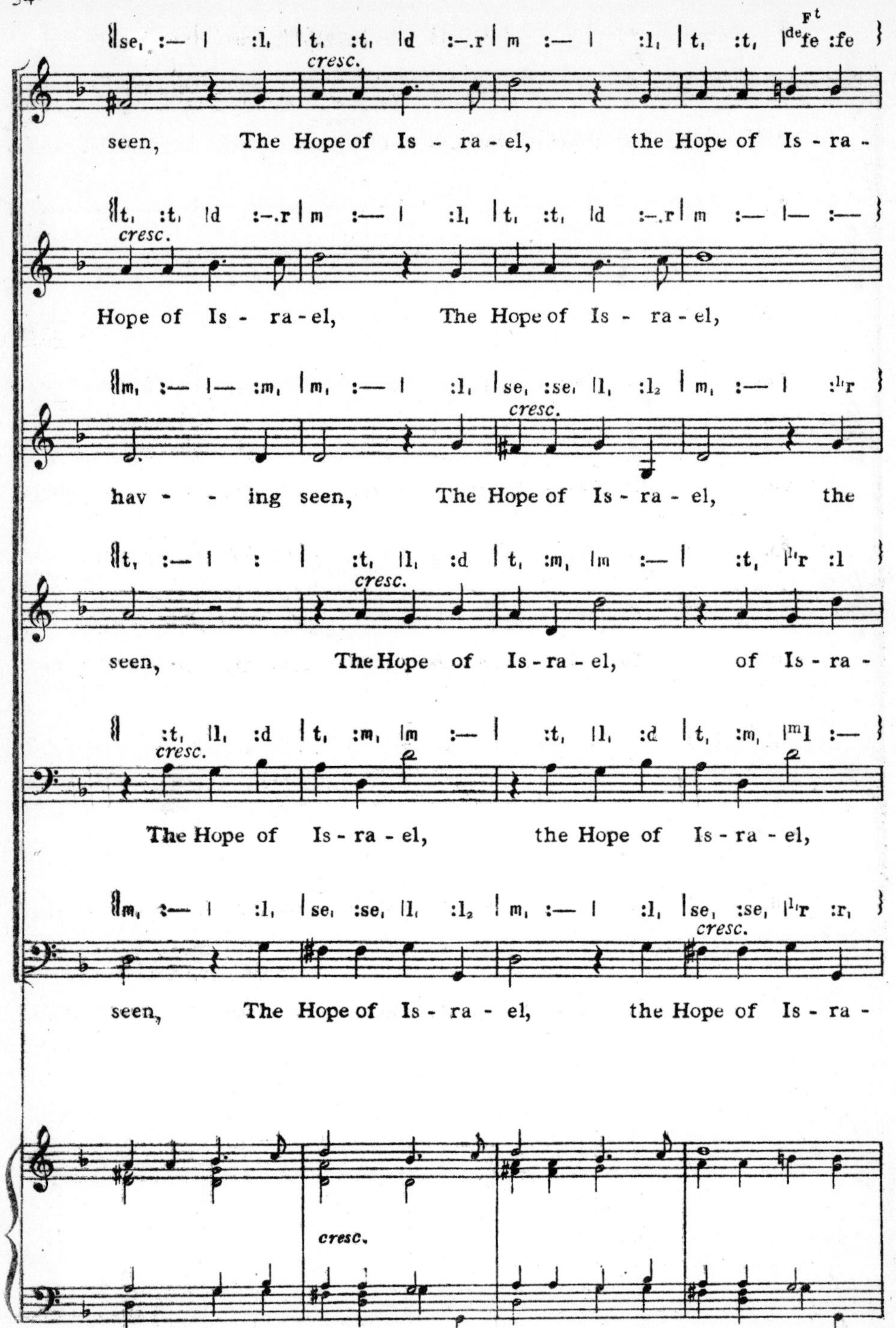
cresc.
seen, The Hope of Is - ra - el, the Hope of Is - ra -
cresc.
Hope of Is - ra - el, The Hope of Is - ra - el,
cresc.
hav - - ing seen, The Hope of Is - ra - el, the
cresc.
seen, The Hope of Is - ra - el, of Is - ra -
cresc.
The Hope of Is - ra - el, the Hope of Is - ra - el,
cresc.
seen, The Hope of Is - ra - el, the Hope of Is - ra -
cresc.

The second verse may be sung more slowly.

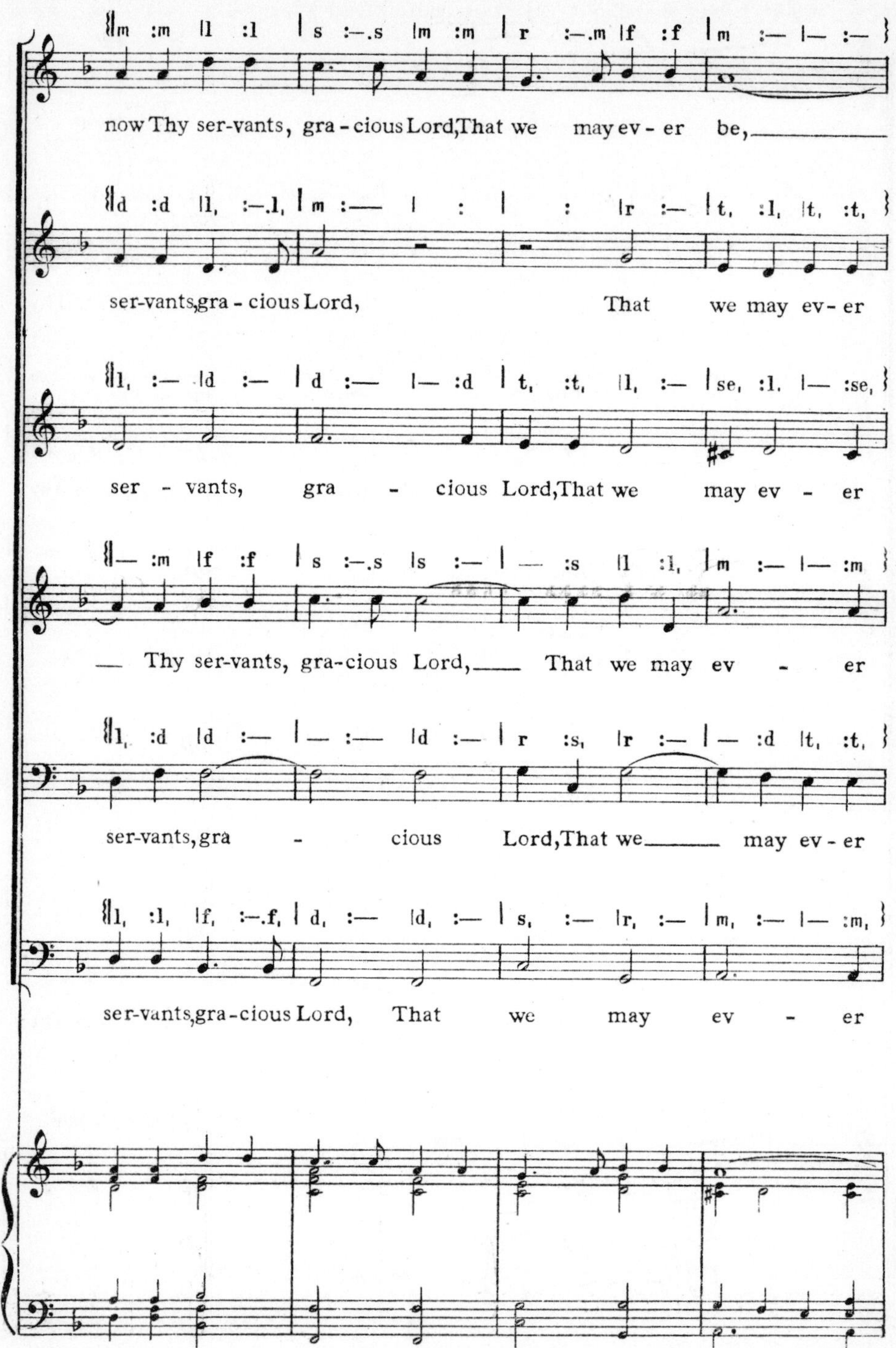
now Thy ser-vants, gra - cious Lord,That we may ev - er be,
ser-vants,gra - cious Lord, That we may ev - er
ser - vants, gra - cious Lord,That we may ev - er
Thy ser-vants, gra-cious Lord, That we may ev - er
ser-vants,gra - cious Lord,That we may ev - er
ser-vants,gra - cious Lord, That we may ev - er

— As once the faith-ful Sim - eon was, Re -
be, As once the faith-ful Sim - eon was,
be, As once the faith - ful Sim - eon
be, As once the faith-ful Sim - eon was,
be, As once the faith-ful Sim - eon
be, As once the faith-ful Sim - eon was, Re -

df Cmi.
-joic - ing but in Thee; And when we must from
Re - joic-ing but in Thee; And when we must from
was, Re - joic - ing but in Thee; And when we must from
— Re - joic-ing but in Thee; And when we must from
was, Re - joic - ing but in Thee; And when we must from
-joic - ing but in Thee; And when we must from

Earth de-par-ture take, de-par-ture take, May gent-ly fall a-
Earth de-par-ture take, de-par - ture take,
Earth de-par-ture take, de-par-ture take, May gent-ly fall a-
Earth de-par-ture take, de-par - ture take, May gent-ly fall a-
Earth de-par-ture take, de-par-ture take,
Earth de-par-ture take, de-par-ture take. May gent-ly fall a-

-sleep, may gent - ly fall a - sleep, may gent-ly fall a-
may gent-ly fall a - sleep, may
-sleep, may fall a - sleep, may
dolce
- sleep, may gent - ly fall a - sleep, may gent-ly
dolce
may gent-ly fall a - sleep,
-sleep, may fall a - sleep, may gent-ly fall a -
(p)
p

cresc. e rit.
f
-sleep, may gent-ly fall a - sleep, And with Thee wake.
cresc. e rit.
f
gent-ly fall a - sleep, And with Thee wake.
cresc. e rit.
f
gent-ly fall a - sleep, And with Thee, and with Thee wake.
cresc. e rit.
f
fall a - sleep, may gent-ly fall a-sleep And with Thee wake.
cresc. e rit.
f
may gent-ly fall a - sleep, And with Thee, and with Thee wake.
cresc. e rit.
f
-sleep, may gent-ly fall a - sleep, And with Thee wake.
cresc e rit.
f

99 WHENCE IS THAT GOODLY FRAGRANCE?

Poem translated by
A. B. RAMSAY
(by kind permission)

Old French Carol
Arranged and harmonised by
ALBERT EDWARD BAKER

s :— :s | m :m :r | d :— :r | m :— :f | s :— :—
- blow - ing, Shep-herds, from flow - 'ry fields in May.
Ch.
Gt.
m :m :r | d :— :s | d' :— :s | l :m :f | s :d :r
Whence is that good - ly fra - grance flow - ing, Steal-ing our
Ch. to Ped.
m :— :s | m :r :— | d :— :— | :m'.r':m'.f' | s' :d'.t :d'.r'
sen - ses all a - way?
Ch. 4ft. in
m' :l .s :l .t | d' :t :l | m :m :r | d :— :s | d' :— :s
mf SOLO
What is that light so bril - liant,
Ped.

l :m :f | s :d :r | m :— :s | m :r :— | d :— :—
break - ing Here in the night a - cross our eyes?
d' :d' :t | l :— :s | d' :l :— | s :— :s | m :m :r
mf
Nev - er so bright the day - star wak - ing, Start - ed to
d :— :r | m :— :f | s :— :— | m :m :r | d :— :s
climb the morn - ing skies! What is that light so
Man.only
Ped.
d' :— :s | l :m :f | s :d :r | m :— :s | m :r :—
f
mf
bril - liant, break - ing Here in the night a - cross our

eyes?
Beth - le-hem!
Ch. add 4ft.
Gt.
Gt. St. Diap.
8va higher
Gt. to Ped.
mp DESCANT
Beth - le-hem! there, in man - ger, find your Re-deem - er, haste a -
there, in man - ger ly - ing, find your Re-deem - er, haste a -
- way. Run ye with ea - ger footsteps hie-ing!
- way. Run ye with ea - ger foot-steps hie - ing!
Ped.

Worship the Saviour born today.
Worship the Saviour born today. Beth-le-hem!
Beth-le-hem! there, in manger, find your Redeemer,
there, in manger lying, find your Redeemer,
haste away.
haste away.
Ch.
Ch. to Ped.
Gt.
Ch.
Gt.
Sw. 8va higher

100 YE THAT DO YOUR MASTER'S WILL

Words by CHAS. WESLEY (1707–88)

ORLANDO GIBBONS (1583–1625)
Edited by H. G. LEY

This anthem to be sung unaccompanied

1. *p* Ye that walk in right - eous - ness.
2. *f* Joy to keep the way of Heav'n.
1. *p* Ye that walk
2. *f* Joy to keep
1. *mf* Gra - cious souls in grace a - bound,
2. *f* Joy to win His wel - come grace,
1. *mf* Gra - cious souls in grace a-bound,
2. *f* Joy to win His welcome grace,
1. *mf* Gra - cious souls in grace a - bound,
2. *f* Joy to win His wel - come grace,
1. *f* Seek the Lord, whom ye have found.
2. *f* Joy to see Him face to face.

First Edition, 1933